Implementing ICD-10-CM/PCS for Hospitals

A Project Guide and Toolkit

Tori E. Sullivan
RHIA, MHA, PMP

Gale C. McNeill
RHIA, CCS

and

Kathleen E. Wall
MS, RHIA

AHIMA PRESS

The Web sites listed in this book were current and valid as of the date of publication. However, Web page addresses and the information on them may change or disappear at any time and for any number of reasons. The user is encouraged to perform his or her own general Web searches to locate any site addresses listed here that are no longer valid.

ISBN-13 978-1-58426-238-1
AHIMA Product No. AC201009

Claire Blondeau, MBA, *Senior Editor*
Katie Greenock, *Editorial and Production Coordinator*
Ashley Sullivan, *Assistant Editor*
Ken Zielske, *Director of Publications*

AHIMA strives to recognize the value of people from every racial and ethnic background as well as all genders, age groups, and sexual orientations by building its membership and leadership resources to reflect the rich diversity of the American population. AHIMA encourages the celebration and promotion of human diversity through education, mentoring, recognition, leadership, and other programs.

American Health Information Management Association
233 North Michigan Avenue, 21st Floor
Chicago, Illinois 60601-5800
ahima.org

Contents

CD-ROM

Chapter 1 Tools:

    Clinical Department Training Plan

    HIM Four-Year Education Plan

    ICD-10 Implementation Project Schedule

    Talking Points for Information Systems Managers

    Talking Points for Senior Managers

    Work Breakdown Structure

Chapter 2 Tools:

    HIM Coding Implementation Checklist

    HIM Coding Source Assessment Tally Tool

    HIM ICD-10-CM Coding Assessment Tool

    Project Budget Planning

    Risk Assessment Template

    Sample Vendor Questions

    Talking Points for Ancillary Department Managers

    Talking Points for Clinical Department Managers

    Talking Points for Healthcare Providers

    Vendor Questionnaire for
        ICD-10-CM_ICD-10-PCS_5010

Chapter 3 Tools:

    Application Testing Results

    Go-Live Plan

    HIM Go-Live Checklist

About the Authors

Tori E. Sullivan, RHIA, MHA, PMP, has been leading complex software implementation projects for healthcare organizations and managing operational divisions providing customer focused supportive and consulting services with software vendors including SoftMed Systems, Inc., and eWebHealth for the past 11 years. She is currently a manager with Capgemini Government Solutions LLC, Healthcare Division, located in Reston, VA. In 2007, Sullivan led the CMS ICD-10 Implementation Assessment Project Team and returned to the consulting industry in 2009. She earned her associate's degree in health information technology in 1997 and her bachelor's degree in health information administration the following year from Dakota State University. Sullivan completed her master's degree in hospital administration with an emphasis on financial systems from the Medical University of South Carolina in 2004.

Gale C. McNeill, RHIA, CCS, is the Supervisor of Coding Education and Quality at Cleveland Clinic Health Systems East Hospitals. She is responsible for coordinating the data quality and education functions for hospital HIM coding professionals. She is actively involved in facility department teams as a contributor to provide coding education to clinical and ancillary providers of care, quality management, revenue integrity, physician documentation improvement, and electronic health record content. In 2007, McNeill was the AHIMA Lead Coding Specialist for the CMS ICD-10 Implementation Assessment Project Team. She earned her associate's degree in health information technology in 1995 and graduated cum laude with a bachelor's degree in health information administration in 2007 from the University of Cincinnati. She is a past president of NOHIMA and active speaker on coding related topics.

Kathleen E. Wall, MS, RHIA, has been a coding professional since 1977. She completed her bachelor of science degree in medical record administration in 1977 from the University of Central Florida and her master's degree in health services management in 1994 from Florida Institute of Technology. Since 1991, her focus has been on data quality serving as both a data quality manager for a five hospital system in Florida as well as spending 13 years with 3M HIS Consulting Services, teaching clinical documentation improvement to physicians, coding professionals, nurses, and ancillary personnel in hundreds of hospitals. In 2007, Wall was an AHIMA coding specialist for the CMS ICD-10 Implementation Assessment Project Team. She has been a presenter at the AHIMA national convention discussing ICD-10-PCS concepts. She has also co-authored articles related to ICD-10 transition and coding specificity with 3M and AHIMA for healthcare journals. She is currently participating in development and maintenance of software for an automated clinical documentation improvement system for 3M.

Acknowledgments

The authors would like to thank AHIMA for giving us an outlet to share our knowledge, particularly Claire Blondeau, our editor. Additionally, we thank the rest of the editorial team at AHIMA for leading and assisting us through the process of writing this book. We also would like to thank the following people for extending their time in guiding us with documenting ideas we believed needed to be included within the text: Dan Rode, AHIMA, who so freely shared his time whenever we asked, and Allison Viola, AHIMA, and Caroline Piselli, 3M, for their readiness assessment tool included in the text. We are grateful for Allison's willingness to provide endless feedback and support throughout this process; AHIMA's eHIM Workgroup for the transition to ICD-10 for participating in a peer review providing us with feedback and suggestions; and Gloryanne Bryant, Kaiser Permanente, for her contributions to the multiple tools included in the text.

We would also like to thank our employers for allowing us to participate in this effort with AHIMA and for recognizing our industry experience and commitment to leading activities for implementing ICD-10-CM/PCS code sets throughout the United States.

Most importantly, we would like to thank our families and friends for their unconditional support, understanding, patience, and forgiveness while we dedicated our (spare) time and energy to this book.

Preface: About ICD-10

What is ICD-10?

International Classification of Diseases, 10th Revision, Clinical Modification (ICD-10-CM) is a clinical modification of the World Health Organization's (WHO) ICD-10, which consists of a diagnostic classification system. ICD-10-CM includes the level of detail needed for morbidity classification and diagnostic specificity in the United States. It also provides code titles and language that complement accepted clinical practice in the United States. As with ICD-9-CM, ICD-10-CM is maintained by the United States National Center for Health Statistics.

When the United States modified ICD-9 to create ICD-9-CM almost 30 years ago, a third volume was added to capture procedure codes. However, instead of appending a short volume to ICD-10-CM, a complete classification, and International Classification of Diseases, 10th Revision, Procedure Coding System (ICD-10-PCS), was developed. This procedural coding system is much more detailed and specific than the short volume of procedure codes included in ICD-9-CM.

The ICD-10-CM system consists of more than 69,000 diagnosis codes, compared to approximately 13,000 ICD-9-CM diagnosis codes. ICD-10-PCS consists of about 73,000 procedure codes. Together the ICD-10-CM and ICD-10-PCS codes have the potential to reveal more about quality of care so that data can be used in a more meaningful way to better understand complications, better design clinically robust algorithms, and better track the outcomes of care. ICD-10-CM

This and additional information about ICD-10 is included on AHIMA's ICD-10 Web site: http://www.ahima.org/icd10/index.html.

and PCS incorporate greater specificity and clinical detail to provide information for clinical decision making and outcomes research.

Why is ICD-9 being replaced?

Developed in the 1970s, the ICD-9-CM coding system no longer fits with the 21st century healthcare system. ICD-9-CM is used for many more purposes today than when it was originally developed and is no longer able to support current health information needs. The United States is virtually the only industrial nation that has not upgraded its morbidity classification system. Upgrading to ICD-10-CM/PCS will improve the United States ability to track and respond to international public health threats, increase the value of the U.S. investment in SNOMED-CT®, and better achieve the benefits of an electronic health record.

Specifically, ICD-9-CM:

- Lacks sufficient specificity and detail
- Is running out of capacity, and the limited structural design cannot accommodate advances in medicine and medical technology and the growing need for quality data
- Is obsolete and no longer reflects current knowledge of disease processes, contemporary medical terminology, or the modern practice of medicine
- Hampers the ability to compare costs and outcomes of different medical technologies
- Cannot support the U.S. transition to an interoperable health data exchange

Replacing ICD-9-CM with ICD-10-CM will better maintain clinical data comparability with the rest of the world, concerning the conditions prompting healthcare services. ICD-10-CM will make it easier to share disease and mortality data at the time when such global data sharing is critical for public health. For example, ICD-10-CM would have better documented the West Nile Virus and SARS complexes for earlier detection and better tracking. ICD-10-CM also provides the ability to track bioterrorism events and other public health outbreaks. The need to replace ICD-9-CM was identified in 1993, when the National Committee on Vital and Health Statistics (NCVHS) reported that ICD-9-CM was rapidly becoming outdated and recommended immediate commitment from the United States to developing a migration to ICD-10-CM for morbidity and mortality coding. Similarly, the Health Care Financing Administration (HCFA), now the Centers for Medicare & Medicaid Services (CMS), recommended that steps should be taken to improve the flexibility of ICD-9-CM or replace it with a more flexible option sometime after the year 2000.

The Value of ICD-10

It is an exciting era of healthcare reform for the United States. The transition to ICD-10-CM and ICD-10-PCS is anticipated to improve the capture of healthcare information and bring the United States in step with coding systems worldwide. For those who prepare appropriately, leveraging the ICD-10 investment will allow organizations to move beyond compliance to achieve competitive advantage.

The value of the transition will be broad, far reaching, and will result in the following:

- Greater coding accuracy and specificity
- Higher quality information for measuring healthcare service quality, safety, and efficiency
- Improved efficiencies and lower costs
- Reduced coding errors
- Greater achievement of the benefits of an electronic health record
- Recognition of advances in medicine and technology
- Alignment of the U.S. with coding systems worldwide
- Improved ability to track and respond to international public health threats

- Enhanced ability to meet HIPAA electronic transaction/code set requirements
- Increased value in the U.S. investment in SNOMED-CT
- Space to accommodate future expansion

Understanding ICD-10

The WHO's ICD (International Classification of Diseases and Related Health Problems), from which ICD-9-CM and ICD-10-CM are derived, is the international standard diagnostic classification for all general epidemiological and many health management purposes. It is used to classify diseases and other health problems recorded on many types of health and vital records, including death certificates and patient medical records. In addition to enabling the storage and retrieval of diagnostic information for clinical and epidemiological purposes, these records also provide the basis for the compilation of national mortality and morbidity statistics by WHO Member States.

The development of WHO's ICD-10 was based on the realization that the great expansion in the use of the ICD necessitated a thorough rethinking of its structure and an effort to devise a stable and flexible classification that would not require fundamental revision for many years to come.

ICD-10-CM is a U.S. clinical modification of the WHO's ICD-10 and is maintained by the National Center for Health Statistics (NCHS). It is a morbidity classification system that classifies diagnoses and other reasons for healthcare encounters. The code structure is alphanumeric, with codes comprised of 3–7 characters.

ICD-10-PCS is a procedural coding system developed under contract by CMS as a replacement of the ICD-9-CM procedural coding system for hospital reporting of inpatient procedures. It has a 7-character alphanumeric code structure.

The United States is the only developed country that has not yet implemented ICD-10 (or a clinical modification) for morbidity, meaning diseases or causes of illness typically coded in a healthcare facility. Since 1999, however, the United States has used ICD-10 only for mortality reporting—the coding of death certificates (typically done by a vital statistics office, not the healthcare facility). Implementing ICD-10-CM will maintain data comparability internationally and between mortality and morbidity data in the United States.

Introduction

The tools provided in this book are suggestions for processes we believe are necessary for successful implementation of ICD-10-CM/PCS and are intended to be a reference for project resources. Each organization will need to identify team members who can fill the roles outlined in this toolkit. Some roles and responsibilities may be shared among a single resource depending on the size of the organization. Larger organizations tend to use more technology than smaller organizations; therefore, this toolkit provides you with a guide to the most comprehensive approach necessary to complete the preparation for ICD-10-CM/PCS. The tools provided in this book are geared toward large hospitals and can be modified to fit your organization's needs and resources. Using these tools will provide continuity during the project. As you progress through the implementation, personnel changes may be required due to resource consumption or changing roles. This process is appropriate and necessary in some cases where the initial resources are not the right fit because of time commitments or knowledge. The goal of each organization should be to complete the project as successfully as possible, and we encourage you to use this toolkit as a guide and make necessary modifications to all provided tools.

ICD-10 Implementation Prerequisite

Transmission of ICD-10-CM/PCS codes requires the expanded functionality and format of X12 transaction standard versions 5010. The new versions replace the current version 4010 for healthcare transactions. The X12 version 5010 replaces version 4010 and includes expanded requirements and specificity for submitted transactions, which are accommodated by the modification of the transaction structure and data contents. X12 version 5010 will require business process modifications and documentation improvements. One significant example includes the requirement to include an indicator for conditions documented as "present on admission" within transaction submissions.

ICD-10-CM/PCS code sets are not supported by the current version 4010, and noncompliance with the modified transaction standards will result in reimbursement consequences. From this point forward, the text will refer to the X12 standard version 5010 as simply 5010. The text assumes organizations have already started work toward understanding the 5010 regulation and requirements, prior to working toward the ICD-10-CM/PCS implementation. The compliance date for implementation of 5010 is January 1, 2012, except for small health plans, which need to comply by the following year.

History of the ICD Systems

Early classifications of diseases focused on classifying causes of mortality. In the early 1900s it was important to also classify diseases to identify morbidity as well. The WHO "History of the development of the ICD" states "The Sixth Decennial Revision Conference marked the beginning of a new era in international vital and health statistics. During the years that the Seventh and Eighth Revisions of the ICD were in force, the use of the ICD for indexing hospital medical records increased rapidly and some countries prepared national adaptations which provided the additional detail needed for this application of the ICD" (WHO Classification Web site).

A Clinical Modification of the Ninth Revision (ICD-9-CM) of the International Classification of Diseases has been in use in the United States since 1979. It was developed by a steering committee at the National Center for Health Statistics and has been updated and modified every year via the ICD-9-CM Coordination and Maintenance Committee Meetings, better known as the Cooperating Parties, encompassing the American Health Information Management

Association, American Hospital Association, and National Center for Health Statistics and Centers for Medicare & Medicaid Services.

The WHO classification Web site states:

> ICD-10 was endorsed by the Forty-third World Health Assembly in May 1990 and came into use in WHO Member States as from 1994. The classification is the latest in a series which has its origins in the 1850s. The first edition, known as the International List of Causes of Death, was adopted by the International Statistical Institute in 1893. WHO took over the responsibility for the ICD at its creation in 1948 when the Sixth Revision, which included causes of morbidity for the first time, was published. The World Health Assembly adopted in 1967 the WHO Nomenclature Regulations that stipulate use of ICD in its most current revision for mortality and morbidity statistics by all Member States.
>
> The ICD is the international standard diagnostic classification for all general epidemiological, many health management purposes and clinical use. These include the analysis of the general health situation of population groups and monitoring of the incidence and prevalence of diseases and other health problems in relation to other variables such as the characteristics and circumstances of the individuals affected, reimbursement, resource allocation, quality and guidelines.
>
> It is used to classify diseases and other health problems recorded on many types of health and vital records including death certificates and health records. In addition to enabling the storage and retrieval of diagnostic information for clinical, epidemiological and quality purposes, these records also provide the basis for the compilation of national mortality and morbidity statistics by WHO Member States.

For more information concerning the history of the classification system see the WHO classifications Web site.

Justification and Timeliness of Implementation

ICD-9-CM is almost 30 years old and is becoming more restrictive when trying to add new codes and accommodating new procedures or technologies. Many chapters in the coding system have reached capacity and will no longer allow additional codes to be added; new codes requiring space are sometimes added to unrelated chapters. As ICD-9-CM code set was not designed to provide the increased level of detail needed to support emerging needs, such as biosurveillance, pay-for-performance programs (P4P), or competitive purchasing, the ICD-10-CM and ICD-10-PCS system will provide the specificity required for these new technologies and existing programs. As noted in the August 22, 2008, proposed rule (73 FR 49827), it is not believed that extending the life of ICD-9-CM by assigning codes to unrelated chapters or purging and reassigning codes no longer used is a long-term solution, and further, that this would perpetuate confusion for coders and data users if hierarchy and code set structure were to continue to be set aside in the issuance of new codes.

Only preliminary work has been done toward the ICD-11 coding system, and no firm timeframes have been outlined by the WHO. The ICD-11 code set provides its basis from ICD-10 with the alpha-numeric framework; therefore, waiting for the projected date of 2020 would make the transition from ICD-9 to ICD-11 more costly and complex. Also considered is the fact that ICD-9-CM is projected to run out of room before the 2020 projected ICD-11 implementation date.

ICD-10-CM Structure

The structure of the alphabetic and tabular indexes is similar to ICD-9-CM. The two parts of the ICD-10-CM index are diseases and injury (including the drugs and chemicals and the neoplasm tables) and external causes of injury. The former V codes in ICD-9-CM are now Z codes included in Chapter 21, Factors Influencing Health Status and Contact with Health Services (Barta 2008, 64).

As illustrated below, ICD-10-CM code structure differs from ICD-9-CM in that it consists of three to seven characters, the first digit being an alpha character and second and third digits being numeric; the fourth and fifth digits may be alpha (not case sensitive) or numeric with a decimal after the third character.

ICD-10-CM FORMAT							
CATEGORY				ETIOLOGY, ANATOMIC SITE, SEVERITY			EXTENSION
X	X	X	.	X	X	X	X

ICD-10-PCS Structure

The procedure coding system for ICD-10-PCS will be used only on inpatient hospital stays. Outpatient surgery and physician outpatient coding will continue to use Current Procedural Terminology® (CPT) for procedure coding. There are seven characters in each ICD-10-PCS (Procedural Coding System) with about 73,000 procedure codes. Each character represents an individual value.

Character 1: Section. There are 16 sections with the general type of procedure identified, for example, Medical Surgical, Placement, Measurement and Monitoring, Imaging, and Nuclear Medicine.

Character 2: Body System. This character defines the general body system on which the procedure is performed, for example Gastrointestinal System, Head and Facial Bones, Male Reproductive System, and Ear/Nose/Sinus.

Character 3: Root Operation. The root operation describes the objective of the procedure. If multiple procedures are performed, more than one code is applied. There are 31 root operations, including Alteration, Bypass, Control, Creation, Dilation, Drainage, Removal, Extirpation, Excision, and Fragmentation.

Character 4: Body Part. This character identifies the specific anatomical site involved in the surgical procedure.

Character 5: Approach. The approach is the technique used to reach the body part at the site of the procedure.

Character 6: Device. This character contains four basic categories: grafts and prostheses; implants; simple or mechanical appliances; and electronic appliances (Bowman 2008, 30).

Character 7: Qualifier. The qualifier designates an additional attribute of the procedure, if applicable. It may identify a type of transplant or the destination site of a bypass.

In each section of PCS, the characters have slightly different meanings to relate to that particular section. The alpha characters are not case sensitive. In the Medical/Surgical Section of PCS, the format is as follows:

ICD-10-PCS FORMAT						
1	2	3	4	5	6	7
Section	Body System	Root Operation	Body Part	Approach	Device	Extension

ICD-10-PCS is made up of three separate parts: tables, an alphabetic index, and a list of codes. The index allows coders to look up the first characters of a code alphabetically, which then refers to a specific location in the tables. The tables are required to obtain the complete code.

There are nuances within some of the ICD-10-PCS language that coders will have to become familiar with, particularly in the root operations. In root operations, there are terms that may have opportunity for further study. Examples include the differences in extirpation, excision, removal, extraction, and resection. Although physicians use these terms interchangeably, in the ICD-10-PCS these terms have exact meanings outlined in each character. This may require the coder to interpret from the body of the operative report, which code will accurately describe the procedure being performed. The body parts may also require a refresher for coding professionals as there is more body site detail represented with the code set.

For more information on ICD-10-PCS, refer to the Centers for Medicare & Medicaid Services ICD-10 Web site.

New Features of ICD-10-CM

Some of the new features are outlined in this section. While not all-inclusive, the following reflects the major changes coders will note when they are learning the new coding system. E codes that were a part of ICD-9-CM are being deleted. As well, some conditions requiring two codes in ICD-9-CM are now combination codes. There are two types of **Excludes Notes**. Excludes1 means NOT CODED HERE: Two conditions cannot occur together. Excludes2 means the condition is NOT INCLUDED HERE. Therefore, it is acceptable to use two codes together to describe a condition.

- **E codes** are not a supplementary classification as in ICD-9-CM. Poisonings and external causes are coded together as one code.
- **Combination codes** are used for:
  —Conditions and common symptoms or manifestations, for example, coronary artery disease with unstable angina
  —Poisonings and external causes
  —Site and stage of decubitus ulcers
  —Severe sepsis with septic shock

- **Expanded code classifications** for several diagnoses including diabetes mellitus and "complications of foreign body left in body following a procedure."
- **Added extensions** for episode of care and expanded detail relevant to ambulatory and managed care encounters (Barta 2008, 64).
- **7th character extensions** delineating episode of care, such as initial, subsequent, sequelae for fractures, injuries, and external causes (Barta 2008, 64).

New Features of ICD-10-PCS

Everything is new regarding ICD-10-PCS when compared to the ICD-9-CM procedure coding system. The ICD-9-CM procedure coding system was incorporated in with the ICD-9-CM diagnosis coding system and was limited by the numeric four digit codes with limited room to expand. The number of characters per code in ICD-10-PCS is expanded to seven alpha-numeric characters (from the four numeric digits in the ICD-9-CM procedure coding system) with a specific meaning for each character. Because each character represents unique meanings depending on the placement of the character, the system has the ability to expand to accommodate the development of new technologies and clinical practices. New codes may be developed as new procedures and devices are approved and put into practice. It is a very specific coding system with the opportunity to facilitate research on outcomes of certain procedures and will be able to more accurately reflect treatment given to patients, thereby accurately portraying the resources utilized for patient care.

General Equivalence Mapping

The General Equivalence Mapping (GEM) files are provided through CMS and are downloadable text files used to provide linkage from ICD-9-CM to ICD-10-CM or from ICD-10-CM to ICD-9-CM code sets. They can be used to analyze and reconcile the differences between the two coding systems as well as serving as reference mappings to help the user navigate the complexity of translating meaning from one code set to the other. There may not always be a one-to-one mapping as the ICD-10-CM coding system is more specific in many cases than ICD-9-CM. One ICD-10-CM code may map to several ICD-9-CM codes and therefore is not a simple "crosswalk" per se, but there are more complex reference mappings between the two systems. For more information on GEM files refer to the CMS ICD-10 Web sites (CMS 2009a).

ICD-10-CM SOURCE	≈	ICD-9-CM
I25.710 Atherosclerosis of autologous vein coronary artery bypass graft(s) with Unstable Angina Pectoris	≈	414.02 Coronary Atherosclerosis of Autologous biological bypass graft AND 411.1 Intermediate Coronary Syndrome

Reimbursement GEM files

The Reimbursement GEM files were developed as a means to allow the ability to map reimbursement MS-DRGs from the ICD-9-CM coding system to the ICD-10-CM and ICD-10-PCS coding systems as it was recognized that payers and providers alike require the ability to study trends and differences in reimbursement as a result of the coding change.

Subsequent to the implementation of the ICD-10 coding system October 1, 2013, all claims discharged on or after that date must be submitted using the ICD-10-CM and ICD-10-PCS code sets. "The Reimbursement Mappings were created to provide a temporary but reliable mechanism for mapping records containing ICD-10-CM diagnoses and ICD-10-PCS procedures to 'reimbursement equivalent' ICD-9-CM diagnoses and procedures, so that while systems are being converted to process ICD-10 claims directly, the claims may be processed by the legacy systems. The ICD-10 diagnoses submitted on the claim are mapped, via application of the Diagnosis Reimbursement Mapping into ICD-9-CM diagnoses used by the ICD-9-CM based reimbursement system. Procedures are mapped in a similar fashion" (CMS 2009b, 1). This user's guide can be found on the CMS ICD-10 Web site.

References

WHO Classification Web site, http://www.who.int/classifications/icd/en/.

Barta, Ann, et al. 2008. ICD-10-CM Primer. *Journal of AHIMA* 79(5):64–66.

Bowman, Sue. 2008. Brushing up on ICD-10-PCS. *Journal of AHIMA* 79(3):30.

Centers for Medicare and Medicaid Services. 2009a. Diagnosis General Equivalence Mappings Documentation and Users Guide, 2009 Version:
http://www.cms.hhs.gov/ICD10/01m_2009_ICD10PCS.asp#TopOfPage
http://www.cms.hhs.gov/ICD10/02m_2009_ICD_10_CM.
asp#TopOfPage
http://www.cms.hhs.gov/ICD10/01m_2009_ICD10PCS.asp#TopOfPage
http://www.cms.hhs.gov/ICD10/02m_2009_ICD_10_CM.
asp#TopOfPage
http://www.cms.hhs.gov/MLNProducts/downloads/ICD-10_GEM_
factsheet.pdf

Centers for Medicare and Medicaid ICD-10 Web site. 2009b. http://www.
cms.hhs.gov/ICD10/

ICD-10-CM/PCS to ICD-9-CM Reimbursement Mappings Documentation and User's Guide 2009 Version
http://www.cms.hhs.gov/ICD10/01m_2009_ICD10PCS.asp#TopOfPage
http://www.cms.hhs.gov/ICD10/02m_2009_ICD_10_CM.
asp#TopOfPage
http://www.cms.hhs.gov/ICD10/01m_2009_ICD10PCS.asp#TopOfPage
http://www.cms.hhs.gov/ICD10/02m_2009_ICD_10_CM.
asp#TopOfPage

Organizational Strategy and Impact Assessment

The first step in the preparation process is to identify and develop an implementation strategy for the overall organization. By developing the implementation strategies early, organizations will define project goals, resource assignments, budgeting estimates, and change management strategies. The resulting activities will produce a project team and develop a project schedule, assessment questionnaires, end-user awareness and training activities, as well as Go-Live preparation plans. This chapter provides a step-by-step guide to developing an organizational approach to managing the implementation of ICD-10-CM and ICD-10-PCS by developing a plan for assessing the impact area and managing the overall project through completion.

Organization-wide Project Strategy

Plan, choice, and goal are all words that define *strategy*. Implementing ICD-10-CM/PCS starts by defining the goals you are working to accomplish along with an action plan necessary to achieve the stated goals. The first step in defining a strategy is to name an executive sponsor and develop an interdisciplinary ICD-10-CM/PCS steering committee for the oversight of the project.

Planning

1. Designate an Executive Sponsor
2. Establish an Interdisciplinary Steering Committee to Oversee ICD-10-CM/PCS Implementation
3. Assign a Project Manager
4. Identify Implementation Strategy
5. Define Project Team Roles and Responsibilities
6. Determine Project Success Factors
7. Develop the Work Breakdown Structure
8. Develop the Project Schedule
9. Develop an Implementation Timeline
10. Create ICD-10-CM/PCS Code Set Impact Awareness Campaign
11. Employ Change Management Strategies
12. Establish the Project Budget
13. Create a Project Team Communications Management Plan
14. Review Organization-wide Strategy with the Team

1. Designate an Executive Sponsor

The executive sponsor, typically a senior management team member, is responsible for financing the project and is tasked with leading the steering committee activities and meetings. As a senior member of the strategic leadership team, the executive sponsor leads the entire implementation for the organization. Once the executive sponsor has been named, the steering committee can be identified. Appendix 1.1, talking points for senior managers, can assist health information management (HIM) leaders in communicating the impact of ICD-10-CM/PCS implementation to organizational strategy managers. A customizable talking points file is included on the CD-ROM.

2. Establish an Interdisciplinary Steering Committee to Oversee ICD-10-CM/PCS Implementation

The interdisciplinary steering committee is responsible for guiding the overall project to ensure the organization and its resources are adequately prepared for the implementation. The committee is required to routinely provide strategic direction, authorize the work of the project, as well as spread buy-in throughout the organization. Members of the steering committee should include senior departmental leadership of the organization directly impacted by the transition. The steering committee members are not members of the project team; instead they are required to provide the sponsorship of the project and are therefore more senior in the organization's leadership. The project management team members essential to the project are required to be much more involved in the daily work of the project than the steering committee members. The steering committee members may include senior leadership for all the impacted areas throughout your organization. Figure 1.1 displays the generic organizational chart for the project leadership.

Some members of the steering committee may also be project team leads for a particular area depending on the size and structure of your organization. The most important role of the steering committee is to authorize the work of the project; therefore, a well-led and productive

Figure 1.1.   Organizational project leadership team

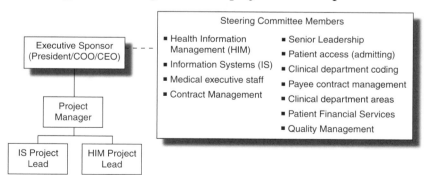

committee is very important to the project success. Steering committee meetings should occur on a regularly established basis and include an agenda to cover the following topics:

- Roll call
- Project update
  —Project timeline
  - Accomplishments since last meeting
  - Upcoming milestones
  - Progress toward milestones
  - Next steps
  —Issues review
- Action items with assignment for committee members
- Wrap-up
- Question and answer session
- Adjournment

3. Assign a Project Manager

Once the executive sponsor and steering committee members have been identified, the planning phase of developing a strategy can begin. The executive sponsor needs to appoint an overall project manager. The skill set for the project manager includes, but is not limited to, the following attributes:

- Excellent communication skills, including preparing and facilitating team meetings ranging from formal presentations to senior executives to routine status meetings with the project team
- Effectively documenting and distributing project communications such as status reports, budget updates, level of effort and task forecasts, issues identification, and resolutions
- The ability to manage, lead, and inspire project team members; resolve conflict; and mentor team members as required

- The ability to think strategically and solve problems related to business processes such as technology and personnel resources, and change management practices
- Experience implementing healthcare technology systems (such as the electronic health record [EHR], electronic medical record [EMR], or clinical systems) that integrate technology throughout multiple departments
- Healthcare experience, in a similar organizational size and structure, operating in a leadership role for at least six years
- At least two years of experience using project management software (such as Microsoft Project), and a track record of establishing project management methodologies and processes
- Other useful knowledge that is valuable but not necessarily required:
  —Knowledge of healthcare financial systems
  —Project Management Professional (PMP) certification
  —Master's degree in healthcare related field

Due to the level of coordination required to complete the ICD-10-CM/PCS implementation, it is important that the project manager identified is authorized to work with multiple levels of the organization. The project manager is responsible for developing and managing the project planning documents as well as facilitating the work in accordance to the project schedule and defined scope.

4. Identify Implementation Strategy

Steering committee members will determine how to organize the ICD-10-CM/PCS project to coordinate the work of teams across the organization. The first order of business is to define the ICD-10-CM/PCS implementation goals and objectives. Each organization has unique requirements due to the various payers' contract parameters; therefore, unique decisions related to the strategy of the project will be made. This is especially true for smaller organizations that may require scaling down some of the tools presented here. Such decisions may include topics regarding risk identification, risk ranking, mitigation tactics, and issue resolution strategies. Defining the project goals and objectives enables your organization to stay focused on determining the best response to any unanticipated issues that arise throughout the implementation. The steering committee along with the project manager should document the goals and objectives in a format that the entire project team and organization can easily reference. In addition to defining the goals and objectives, the executive project leadership should commit the additional time and effort required, above and beyond the daily responsibilities, to allocate appropriate resources to complete the work of the project.

5. Define Project Team Roles and Responsibilities

Once the project manager has been identified and appointed, the steering committee will identify the project team members. Representatives from HIM, coding, finance (reimbursement), information services (IS), clinical divisions, and any other areas impacted by the project should be included on the project team.

Due to the significance in the areas of HIM and information technology (IT), the project team should at least include lead positions for both of these areas. The team members will be responsible for identifying, developing, and completing their department's work on the project. Tasks can be documented initially on a work breakdown structure (WBS) for each project team (HIM, IS, and others) and assigned a project team member to complete the teaks. (A detailed discussion of WBS is included in the next section.) All project tasks identified on each WBS will roll up into the overall project schedule. Team members assigned to specific tasks on the project schedule are required to complete the work as outlined, or notify the project manager to reallocate the assignment.

6. Determine Project Success Factors

Upon completion of the project, the leadership and project team evaluates whether the project was a success or not. Establishing incremental, milestone success factors throughout the duration of the project will assist the team members to stay focused on the goals and stay within the scope of the project throughout its duration. Goals for a specific organization will be determined by the project team and led by the steering committee. Following are some examples of success factors:

- Software modifications were 80 percent identified through assessment activities
- Vendors/contractors modified systems according to estimates within a 3 percent estimate margin
- Software modifications were tested and passed with a 2 percent error margin
- Staff education was completed on time and on budget
- Coding staff met testing and preparation activity estimates outlined in the Go-Live plan
- Additional staff received training and completed testing activities with an 80 percent pass rate
- Claims submission rates decreased no lower than the forecasted rate 30 days post Go-Live
- Reimbursement rates decreased no lower than the forecasted rate 30 days post Go-Live
- Post Go-Live coding audit verified use of expanded code set as expected in the Go-Live plan

The above listed success criteria are *samples* and not meant as a real-world standard. Each organization will develop success criteria specific to the facility, resources, staffing, and financial situation. Throughout the duration of the project, the success factors and project scope should be discussed and adjusted as determined by the steering committee. The scope of the project can extend (creep) beyond the original objectives and goals, impacting the project in positive or negative ways. Scope creep is typically considered to be negative because it is a result of mismanaged objectives or deliverables. If project work is requiring resources to expand beyond their original allocation to the project, the project scope has crept. The outcome of project deliverables may also be an added software feature, due to a vendor upgrade, for example, that requires additional work on the vendor side. Even if the new feature/functionality is an added benefit to the organization, the project scope has crept beyond the original plan. Management of project deliverables and budget are just as important as the management of scope creep. In a project of this size and with the volume of interactions, it is very easy for deliverables to be *gold plated*. Gold plating means adding features, functionality, resources, etc. to a deliverable defined within the project because someone has identified it to be a benefit without formal approval from the project manager and steering committee. Anytime additional features, functionality or processes improvements are added to the scope (original objectives) and require additional resources, the project manager must be aware of the expanded scope and incorporate the additional feature, function and/or process into the project through a formal approval process. Scope creep can overextend project resources and deflate project budgets and should be taken very seriously by the project team. By keeping an eye on the project goals and scope, team members can mitigate issues that may negatively impact the overall project.

7. Develop the Work Breakdown Structure

The WBS is a listing of all implementation and Go-Live preparation activities (deliverables) required to meet the project milestones. Team members familiar with the project and assessment findings should brainstorm all deliverables identified for the project. Tasks can be entered into the WBS spreadsheet rows listing the deliverables, dependencies, and assigned resources. See table 1.1 for a sample WBS template; a customizable file is included on the CD-ROM. Project deliverables should be identified specific to each project team (such as the HIM and IS teams) and should be identified in an order of accomplishment under identified project phases.

8. Develop the Project Schedule

Once the deliverables have been identified, the WBS from each project team can be consolidated and rolled up into the project schedule

Table 1.1. Sample work breakdown structure (WBS)

Milestone	Task	Dependencies	Hour Estimate	Resource	Start Date	Planned Completion	Estimate to Completion	Actual Completion	Status
1									
2									
3									
4									
5									
6									
7									
8									
9									
10									

by the project manager. The detailed project schedule should have a start date (as soon as possible) and include tasks that roll up into deliverables, which roll up into milestones, and in turn roll up into project phases. Tasks with the longest duration to complete, if altered, will result in a change to scope—schedule, budget, resources, project deliverables—and should be identified on the critical path (CP) of the project schedule. The project communication schedule should also be listed on the project schedule. Microsoft Project® is a common tool to consolidate both WBS files and an organizational project schedule; however, there are plenty of other project management software tools that will produce the same result. The sample ICD-10 implementation project schedule included on the CD-ROM can be used as a start; however, you may have a sample your organization has used in the past for a similarly scaled project. See figure 1.2 for a one-page snapshot of this tool, and Appendix A for the complete item. (All tools included in the CD-ROM are customizable documents that a project team would continue to update throughout the course of the project.) The project schedule included here is designed to be a high-level plan for an organization to expand upon (or, for smaller organizations, to scale down) once the team included in the WBS identifies each task required for the overall project. The project schedule is initially approved as the baseline schedule by the steering committee. The project manager can revise the baseline schedule at designated intervals or milestones approved by the steering committee throughout the project.

9. Develop an Implementation Timeline

Once your organization has established the project team and structure, identified the project deliverables through the WBS and project schedule, the project timeline can be established by working backward from the Centers for Medicare & Medicaid (CMS) Final Rule Go-Live date of October 1, 2013. However, each organization must determine its own start date based on the time required to complete the project work internally. Knowing the implementation date, scheduling work should begin *as soon as possible*. A suggested timeline

Figure 1.2. Sample ICD-10 implementation project schedule

ID	Task Name	Duration	Start	Finish	Resource Names
1	ICD-10 Implementation Schedule	1353 days	Fri 1/16/09	Tue 3/25/14	Executive Sponsor
2	Final Regulations	792 days	Fri 1/16/09	Mon 1/30/12	Health and Human Services
3	Published Rule - ICD-10, v5010, vD.0 and v.3.0	1 day	Fri 1/16/09	Fri 1/16/09	CMS
4	Rule effective	1 day	Tue 3/17/09	Tue 3/17/09	CMS
5	Version 5010/D.0/3.0 Activities	542 days	Fri 1/1/10	Mon 1/30/12	Steering Committee
10	Planning	62 days	Mon 6/1/09	Tue 8/25/09	Steering Committee
11	Kick-off Meeting	1 day	Mon 6/1/09	Mon 6/1/09	Executive Sponsor,Core Project Team,Steering C
12	Develop Project Documents	50 days	Tue 6/2/09	Mon 8/10/09	Steering Committee
20	Submit Project Documents for Approval	36 days	Tue 6/23/09	Tue 8/11/09	Steering Committee
25	Approve Project Documents	45 days	Wed 6/24/09	Tue 8/25/09	Steering Committee
30	Communication Management	1023 days	Wed 1/6/10	Fri 12/6/13	Steering Committee
31	Steering Committee Status Meetings	1001 days	Fri 2/5/10	Fri 12/6/13	Steering Committee
79	Core Project Team Status Meeting	981 days	Wed 1/6/10	Wed 10/9/13	Core Project Team
277	Outreach Communications	481 days	Mon 1/2/12	Mon 11/4/13	Executive Sponsor
301	Impact Assessment (Gap Analysis)	60 days	Wed 8/26/09	Tue 11/17/09	Steering Committee
302	Develop Assessment Questionnaires	20 days	Wed 8/26/09	Tue 9/22/09	Project Manager
307	Distribute Assessment Questionnaires	40 days	Wed 9/23/09	Tue 11/17/09	Project Manager
314	Implementation (Design)	535 days	Wed 9/30/09	Tue 10/18/11	Steering Committee
315	Collect Assessment Questionnaires	55 days	Wed 9/30/09	Tue 12/15/09	Project Manager
322	Analyze Results & Develop Action Plan	135 days	Wed 10/14/09	Tue 4/20/10	Project Manager
329	Software System Replacement Process	390 days	Wed 4/21/10	Tue 10/18/11	Project Manager
334	Go-Live Preparation (Development and Testing)	915 days	Wed 4/21/10	Tue 10/22/13	Steering Committee
335	Develop Go-Live Plan	30 days	Wed 5/4/11	Tue 6/14/11	Project Manager
336	Distribute Go-Live Plan	1 day	Wed 6/15/11	Wed 6/15/11	Project Manager
337	Execute Project Plans	898 days	Wed 4/21/10	Fri 9/27/13	Project Manager
338	Initial ICD-10-CM and ICD-10-PCS Training and Education	60 days	Thu 6/16/11	Wed 9/7/11	HIM Project Lead
343	Internal Software System Modifications	360 days	Thu 9/8/11	Wed 1/23/13	IT Project Lead
361	Internal System Testing and Validation	110 days	Thu 1/24/13	Wed 6/26/13	IT Project Lead
374	External Software System Modifications	420 days	Wed 4/21/10	Tue 11/29/11	IT Project Lead
392	External System Testing and Validation	370 days	Wed 11/30/11	Tue 4/30/13	IT Project Lead
405	Go-Live Training	155 days	Thu 1/24/13	Wed 8/28/13	HIM Project Lead
418	Final Go-Live Preparation Activities	108 days	Wed 5/1/13	Fri 9/27/13	
422	Implementation Go-Live	16 days	Tue 10/1/13	Tue 10/22/13	Steering Committee
423	Code Charts Using ICD-10-CM and ICD-10-PCS Codes	1 day	Tue 10/1/13	Tue 10/1/13	HIM Project Resource
424	Transmit ICD-10-CM and ICD-10-PCS Data	5 days	Wed 10/2/13	Tue 10/8/13	Project Manager
427	Verify Data Transmits Correctly	5 days	Wed 10/9/13	Tue 10/15/13	IT Project Lead
430	Verify Reports Generate Correctly	5 days	Wed 10/16/13	Tue 10/22/13	
433	Post Implementation Activities	115 days	Wed 10/16/13	Tue 3/25/14	Executive Sponsor
434	Evaluate Project Results	15 days	Wed 10/16/13	Tue 11/5/13	Core Project Team
435	Complete Project De-Brief	10 days	Wed 11/6/13	Tue 11/19/13	Project Manager
438	Identify Operational On-going Changes	90 days	Wed 11/20/13	Tue 3/25/14	Executive Sponsor
441	Celebrate Project Success	1 day	Wed 11/20/13	Wed 11/20/13	Core Project Team,Steering Committee,Executive

for implementation activities can include the following milestones for each year of the project:

- Year one—Complete impact assessment
- Year two—Complete implementation activities
- Year three—Complete testing and training activities
- Year four—Complete preparation activities and Go-Live

10. Create ICD-10-CM/PCS Code Set Impact Awareness Campaign

The ICD-10-CM/PCS implementation will significantly impact specific areas within each organization; therefore, communication should establish awareness about the ICD-10-CM/PCS code sets impact throughout the organization. Resources have been aware of various levels of information about ICD-10-CM/PCS for many years. The organization-wide implementation strategy should include creating and distributing communication about the ICD-10-CM/PCS code sets' impact to enhance the education of the transition throughout the organization. The project team should develop an organization-wide impact awareness campaign to implement during the planning phase. This campaign will serve to educate the organizational resources, senior managers, IS teams, clinical resources, and medical staff about ICD-10-CM/PCS, potential departmental impacts, and estimated project timelines, with key milestones identified. In addition to awareness, the campaign also should serve to minimize any anticipated fear, apprehension, and reaction.

Campaign materials should be developed by the project team and distributed throughout the organization at regular intervals for the duration of the project. Initial materials may include posters, brochures, Web site postings, or blogs describing the regulations and required changes. As the project progresses, materials should include information regarding the activities the organization is pursuing, milestones achieved, and next steps. The end goal should be communicated to assist with gaining buy-in from the resources throughout the organization.

11. Employ Change Management Strategies

The ICD-10-CM/PCS transition and 5010 implementation require every healthcare organization to make changes to common processes. Coders will be required to learn a new system, physician documentation may require modification to provide additional detail (for example, injury codes require episode information), and the finance department will experience changes to reimbursement standards. No direct impact to the reimbursement rates for coded data is expected at this time; however, organizations can initially expect an increased rate of denials and decreased coding productivity resulting in direct financial impact. The American Health Information Management Association (AHIMA) estimates that the learning curve for experienced staff in place would be about six months. Therefore, understanding the challenges to implement and strategically manage change is extremely important to the success of the ICD-10-CM/PCS project. Change tends to instill fear in staff unsure of the outcome. Strategies to manage change and work to minimize the fear factor are beneficial to organizations and are highly recommended.

12. Establish the Project Budget

All project activities require resources and therefore require funding, thus the importance of a managed budget. Once the project scope and risks are identified, the ICD-10-CM/PCS transition budget can be estimated. A comprehensive budget includes funding for contingencies in addition to reserves since all projects require some change during the duration of the work. It is essential to develop a project review process as a part of the overall project management plan. The use of the contingency and reserve funding should be agreed upon by the steering committee and applied only when necessary.

13. Create a Project Team Communications Management Plan

Successful projects are direct results of successful communication. The project communication plan should include the following:

- The schedule of when and where the project team will meet
- What topics will be covered each meeting
- Who will send the agenda
- Who will document the meeting minutes
- Who will distribute the communication

Most project communication is led by the project manager; however, this project will mandate many subprojects and those may be led by various team members. Each project meeting should be documented and results incorporated into the overall project communication. Marketing of the project should also be considered and discussed as a part of the communication management plan.

14. Review Organization-wide Strategy with the Team

The final step in developing an organization-wide strategy is to assign the work of the project to begin. A kick-off meeting should be conducted early in the project to bring all project resources together to review the project plans and associated assignment of resources.

Impact Assessment Strategy and Activities

ACTION STEPS

1. Impact Assessment Strategy
2. Impact Assessment Activities

1. Impact Assessment Strategy

An assessment of the areas affected by the transition to 5010 and ICD-10-CM/PCS is one of the project team's initial activities to identify technology modifications, outreach, and education required, as well as operational process modifications to efficiently implement the new code set. The assessment activities include conducting outreach and education and data collection strategies, such as conference calls, in-person meetings, and electronic surveys. Assessment questions will collect findings of information related to the work required in preparation for the transition and will enable the organization to analyze areas where it is most at risk regarding the ICD-10-CM and ICD-10-PCS implementation.

The project team should communicate to the senior management that software vendors must work with internal resources to complete the modifications required to comply with the regulations. Incorporating communication to vendors regarding risk analysis is imperative to ensure proper completion of testing activities. It is in the best interest of each organization to build time into the schedule for completing a detailed systems assessment for mutual understanding of all system modifications required to comply with both 5010 and ICD-10-CM/PCS, even if the work required to adjust the systems is not required by its staff but is instead vendor-based.

The distribution method for the assessment questions should also be included in the IS department's strategy, customized to the organization, and developed by the project team. This assessment would include a listing of resources knowledgeable about the regulatory changes to ensure that all areas are covered during the assessment process. Methods to distribute the assessment questionnaires may include one or more of the following:

- E-mail surveys focused to each specific department or service area
- Intranet Web surveys for all staff

- Paper surveys distributed via interoffice mail, U.S. Postal Service, or fax
- In-person or telephone surveys conducted through interviews and direct dialog

Survey distribution and collection should be a scheduled and tracked process as every area included in the assessment needs to be accounted for in order to avoid missing important areas or systems. Each organization will need to identify the most appropriate means of delivering survey tools and collecting the survey data.

2. Impact Assessment Activities

Project leads from the HIM and IS departments will manage and conduct an impact assessment. The goal of the impact assessment is to determine the risk areas within the organization. Due to the level of effort and resource commitment required to complete the assessment activities, such extensive examination would be unusual to conduct under any other circumstances. Organizations should take this opportunity to review and assess current processes in comparison to best practice methodology and identify opportunities to expand service offerings. ICD-10-CM/PCS implementation provides an ideal opportunity to identify and make otherwise unrecognized, needed changes within the organization. Optimizing operations and improving service level offerings and patient care can assist organizations with reaching long-term goals far outreaching ICD-10-CM/PCS implementation.

The process of identifying software currently using or producing data related to ICD codes is critical to begin as soon as possible because of the varied responses you may receive regarding the level of effort and the potential to modify systems. Some systems will require minimal effort to accommodate the field length and logic alterations, while other legacy systems will require extensive changes to comply with the regulation standards. Organizational use of coded data can be hidden in systems utilized by many departments and can easily be overlooked. Some systems produce reports with diagnosis or proce-dures listed by name instead of code and end-users may not realize the data generated behind the scenes include ICD codes. Therefore, it is best to conduct an assessment of *every* department within the organization. Assessment surveys related to software systems should include questions regarding all of the following areas:

- Current and future use of ICD-9-CM and 4010
- Required modifications to accommodate 5010 and ICD-10-CM/PCS
- Ability for systems to comply with future regulation require-ments
- Ability for systems to process both ICD-9-CM and ICD-10-PCS code sets simultaneously
- Resource (staff and budget) requirements, including time, to modify software systems
- Identified and unknown risks with modifying applications

The CD-ROM includes sample tools, many of which are shown in figures throughout the book, to assist with the process of creating appropriate assessment tools for your organization. We encourage you to develop assessment questions to best fit your audience. Some answers to the survey questions will need to be further clarified and revisited most likely as a result of the information collected and could lead to additional follow-up surveys. This is particularly relevant when discussing software systems and modifications required for the regula-tions. In some instances, it may be helpful to distribute an initial set of questions that discuss current involvement at a higher level and then plan to develop follow-up questions focused in specific areas on a much more detailed level.

The detailed assessment should cover ICD-9-CM usage questions as well as questions related to software system use of 4010. Questions appropriate to cover all aspects of 5010 should be further researched by your organization, as they are not covered in depth within this text. However, both 5010 and ICD-10-CM/PCS final regulations published by the Department of Health and Human Services (HHS) will require modifications to software systems, procedure modifications, and resource training. It is therefore most efficient to combine all questions about both regulation changes into a single assessment tool. The data collected through the assessment phase will include information directly related to one rule or the other, as well as information that will impact both regulations. One example is staff training. As detailed in the next sections, the training and staff preparation to implement ICD-10-CM/PCS is much more extensive than the training necessary for 5010. The change to ICD-10-CM/PCS will require more extensive procedural changes and software modifications than 5010, although the latter must be implemented first. The assessment questionnaires should be distributed throughout the organization, including the departments that are initially believed to have no impact, as well as to vendors and associated contractors of the organization.

The CD-ROM also includes talking points that will assist with educating the various departments and vendors regarding the required modifications and a vendor checklist that can be used as a guide to developing questions specific to your organization and associated software systems modifications for both the 5010 and ICD-10-CM/PCS requirements.

The survey and interview questions will determine the current state of operational processes, technology using ICD coded data, and current knowledge and awareness of ICD-10-CM/PCS codes, and identify preparation requirements for implementing the new code set. Additional information—such as financial estimates to accommodate modifications regarding technology, processes, and people—will be collected during the assessment process and used to update the initial project budget. The assessment findings and recommendations from each department, vendor, and contractor interviewed during the process will provide the project team with information necessary to develop the updated project schedules, task outlines, and milestones preliminarily scoped by the project team earlier in the project.

Information Systems Strategy and Impact Assessment

ACTION STEPS

1. Organize Project Team and Identify Project Tasks
2. Create an Awareness Campaign
3. Assess the Impact to Systems and Technologies
4. Review Vendor and Third-party contracts

The information systems used throughout the organization will require an assessment or gap analysis to evaluate the impact and work required to accommodate 5010 and ICD-10-CM/PCS on existing and future systems. The IS department will have significant responsibility on this project, and the team will need to be organized in its approach to completing the project activities within the allocated timeframe. Although the Go-Live date may seem to be far off in the future, vendor organizations should make systems updates to accommodate the requirements. The IS departments cannot assume vendors will complete all testing activities required for your own organization and should prepare to communicate and possibly train the vendors for necessary changes. The modifications required for the 5010 and ICD-10-CM/PCS changes are complex and will require multi-layered testing activities. IS resources will be an integral part of the implementation activities project and are vital to the success of the project.

1. Organize Project Team and Identify Project Tasks

The first step in the IS assessment process is to identify the project team lead for the department and assign the project team resources. Team members will need to be oriented and educated about the ICD-10-CM/PCS code sets, including field lengths, logic, and hierarchical structure used for both code sets. Figure 1.3 is a sample organizational chart for the IS project team.

Figure 1.3.   IS project team

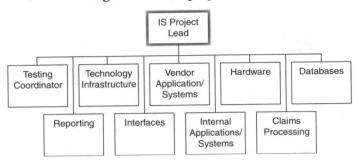

Additional system changes are required to accommodate 5010 and must be explored further by each organization. The IS project lead is responsible for spearheading activities related to the software systems affected by the implementation. The IS lead will need to report to the project manager the appropriate amount to dedicate to these activities.

The IS project team will need to develop a WBS specific to the tasks required to identify, assess, modify, test, and validate software systems and associated processes throughout the organization. The tasks identified in the WBS should have durations and resources allocated to the best of the project team's knowledge. The WBS from IS will be merged with the WBS from the HIM resources as well as the steering committee's WBS to identify and remove all duplicate activities. The project manager will work with the IS team to include all IS WBS activities on the schedule and to create the associated project planning documents.

2. Create an Awareness Campaign

In addition to the coding audience, the IS resources will be required to understand the structural differences between ICD-9-CM and ICD-10-CM/PCS code sets and between the 4010 and 5010 regulatory requirements. Team members most likely will work closely with the HIM resources on the project; however, they cannot depend on coding knowledge alone to identify impacts to the systems and technologies. Appendix 1.2 includes talking points for training the IS resources about the ICD-10-CM/PCS code sets and project considerations in preparation for the assessment activities. (Talking points for other departments are included elsewhere in this book and also on the CD–ROM.) Training topics focused on IT resources should include:

- Introduction to implementation strategy and timelines
- Code format changes between ICD-9-CM and ICD-10-CM/PCS
- Activities required to support the timeline, including comprehensive system inventory and assessment
- Review of project risks

3. Assess the Impact to Systems and Technologies

A comprehensive systems audit should be conducted to identify all applications and technology that currently uses, interacts, or plans to use and interact with ICD-10-CM/PCS data. The systems identified by the audit will require an impact analysis to determine specific modifications required for the implementation. The tasks to implement 5010 should include a gap analysis between the current technology and future standards required for ICD-10-CM/PCS compliance. The project lead should be prepared that the assessment outcome will identify a wide range of tasks and resource commitments, the most significant of which may be a need to acquire and implement new technology to meet the regulatory standards.

a. Conduct a Systems Inventory

Some organizations may first conduct an inventory of all applications and systems within the organization that use, process, or store ICD-9-CM codes. The results of a systems inventory process would also be added to the assessment findings, as systems identified to be impacted by the implementation of ICD-10-CM/PCS will require further analysis to determine the specific changes and level of effort required.

b. Develop Assessment Questions

A comprehensive assessment of all systems and technologies includes developing a list of questions regarding usage of ICD-10-CM/PCS codes and data elements along with the 5010 transaction requirements that will need to be answered by internal data engineers and vendor contacts. Questions regarding both regulations should be developed and distributed jointly with the IS lead to streamline the assessment activities and minimize the time to complete implementation and testing activities. Specific knowledge about the structure and architecture of existing applications and databases will be required to answer system assessment questions. Assessment questions will need to be compiled specifically for the following topics related to ICD-9-CM usage:

- Software systems currently using ICD-9-CM codes and planned to use ICD-10-CM/PCS codes
- Staff currently using ICD-9-CM codes and planned to use ICD-10-CM/PCS codes
- Staff currently using data or data elements derived from ICD-9-CM codes and planned to use ICD-10-CM/PCS codes
- Future plans for implementing and using new technology or modules within current technology that use ICD-9-CM codes and that would use ICD-10-CM/PCS codes

Figure 1.4 includes a sample of detailed questions for vendors, and a customizable file is included on the CD-ROM.

The sample listing in figure 1.4 is a starting point to modify to be specific to your organization to cover all systems currently used at your facility. The ICD-10 Preparation Checklist (Bowman and Zeisset 2007) outlines additional questions to cover during the assessment activities. This reference is included in Appendix B.

c. Conduct a Comprehensive Systems Assessment

The assessment activities should start with third-party applications, as their work required to complete the assessment and required modifications is out of the direct control of your organization. If your organization employs vendors, vendor readiness is of critical importance

Figure 1.4.   Sample vendor questions

- Does this application currently use ICD-9-CM codes?
- If no, is the application planned to use ICD-9-CM or ICD-10-CM or ICD-10-PCS codes?
- What date will the system begin to use ICD codes?
- How is the system currently using ICD-9-CM codes?
- What departments are using the data collected or provided by this application?
- Identify other systems that link to this application to transmit ICD-9-CM codes.
- Provide a brief description of how you plan to accommodate the ICD-10-CM and/or ICD-10-PCS code sets in this application.
- Specify whether or not the application will be able to accommodate the ICD-10-CM, ICD-10-PCS, and ICD-9-CM code sets in a Dual Use testing strategy.
- Specify how the ICD-9-CM codes will be disabled in the transactions once the ICD-10-CM and ICD-10-PCS code sets are in full effect.
- Specify how the version of this application compatible with ICD-10-CM and ICD-10-PCS codes will handle ICD-9-CM codes interfaced from other applications (for example, will ICD-9-CM codes be cross-walked to ICD-10-CM or ICD-10-PCS codes?).
- List all vendor-supported interfaces that will be affected by the ICD-10-CM or ICD-10-PCS code sets and how each will be remediated.
- List all steps that this facility must perform to implement the ICD-10-CM and ICD-10-PCS code sets in this application.
- Specify the date that the application compatible with ICD-10-CM and ICD-10-PCS code sets will be available for testing.
- Specify the earliest date that current software version can be upgraded to accommodate the ICD-10-CM and ICD-10-PCS code sets.
- Specify how long it will take to implement the version compatible with ICD-10-CM and ICD-10-PCS codes.
- Attach your proposed project schedule for implementing the compatible version for supporting ICD-10-CM and ICD-10-PCS code sets.
- Specify the vendor resources required to upgrade the current software version in preparation for ICD-10-CM and ICD-10-PCS code sets.
- List any facilities within this organization that are behind on the current application releases and how many upgrades will be required to bring each facility's applications current.
- Indicate the resources that are available or can be recommended to assist with the application upgrade (for example, third party contractors/consultants).

to several tasks on the project, including testing and verification that will directly impact other critical project tasks. Therefore, vendor tasks automatically fall on the critical path (CP) for the project because of the potential to directly affect three key project elements: scope, time, and cost. Tasks on the CP, such as these, are likely to take the most time to complete and use the majority of the project budget. You may find that some vendors will require you to purchase and implement an upgrade to your existing system to accommodate ICD-10-CM/PCS code sets. Organizations should not depend on vendors to complete the required assessment activities on their own. Lack of preparation and testing on the vendor systems will directly impact organizational revenue; therefore, each organization must complete independent assessment and planning activities.

Both internal and vendor legacy systems may fall into the category of either being too expensive or unable to be updated to accommodate the expanded regulations. The process of working with vendors and internal systems engineers to identify modification requirements may be quite time consuming and costly; therefore, the earlier you begin your assessment activities of IS, the more time you will have to identify the best options for your organization. Once these activities have been completed, the project team can review the findings and complete the risk assessment and gap analysis.

4. Review Vendor and Third-party Contracts

The organization should identify the appropriate resources to review vendor and third-party contracts in detail to determine if modifications are necessary to change systems or procedures required by the regulations. Some vendors may not be able to comply with the 5010 transaction formatting or ICD-10-CM/PCS code sets and will need to be replaced, thus requiring the identification, review, negotiation, and acquisition of replacement technology or service providers within the project timeline. This process can be run concurrently with the assessment activities to work toward completing all review activities and allow the most time possible to complete modification activities.

Health Information Management
Strategy and Impact Assessment

1. Develop an HIM Project Team
2. Designate a Team Leader
3. Organize the HIM Project Team
4. Develop an HIM Project Plan
5. Create the Work Breakdown Structure

HIM departments exist in most organizations with business functions related to managing the dissemination and delivery of healthcare information and data derived from the clinical information to manage patient care. The business functions involved with the reporting of coded data created from health information are usually performed within the HIM department. The coded data are subsequently used and disseminated to and from hospitals, physicians, clinical departments, other healthcare providers, payers, and accounting for reimbursement, and also for decision making, research, and other purposes both internally and externally.

1. Develop an HIM Project Team

During the ICD-10-CM/PCS impact assessment phase, the organizational steering committee will control the time, money, and scope of the project. The steering committee will assign various subproject groups, including a representative project group from HIM. In most hospitals and health-information–related organizations, the HIM department is a highly impacted area when dealing with changes related to the content of data derived from personal health information created within the daily business functions. The HIM project team members will have specific predefined objectives set by the steering committee relating to the implementation of ICD-10-CM and ICD-10-PCS.

Before implementation, it is necessary to assess the HIM department's business processes to identify both internal and external customers' use of coded data. The HIM project team will utilize various assessment tools, such as clinical department coding surveys, clinical department interviews, or coding workflow analysis, to identify what risks exist to and the degree of impact on each department's business functions which uses coded data services. Also, during the assessment phase the HIM department may also be assessing nonclinical external areas, such as marketing and registries, which may utilize reports of certain disease specific patient statistics created by coded data for organizational planning. This type of assessment activities process is an example of work that will be conducted by the HIM project team. Figure 1.5 is a sample organizational chart for the HIM project team.

2. Designate a Team Leader

The first step in creating the HIM project team is to designate a team leader. The project manager should work with the steering committee to designate the team leader. The project team leader is tasked with identifying the HIM team participants, organizing the work of the project along with the project manager, and facilitating the work of the project assigned to the HIM project team. Activities assigned to the HIM project team leader may include developing the HIM project plan, authorizing and distributing project tasks, organizing the project team meetings, and reporting the progress of the team's work to the organization's project manager and/or steering committee.

Figure 1.5.   HIM project team

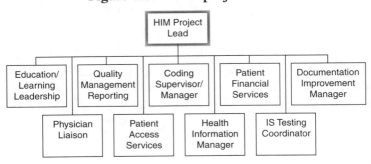

The HIM project team leader may also be the same HIM representative who is assigned to the organizational steering committee. For instance, the HIM director may participate in the project steering committee and serve as the HIM project team leader. Due to the workload of the HIM project team leader, this position may be designated outside of the HIM director position. For example, depending on the size of the facility, the project team leader at a hospital may be the HIM assistant director or coding manager.

3. Organize the HIM Project Team

The HIM project team is a subgroup of the organizational project steering committee. The HIM project team key stakeholders should include, at a minimum, the following:

- Coding supervisor/manager
- Health information manager
- Patient access service representative
- Patient financial services representative
- Quality management reporting representative
- Documentation improvement manager
- IS representative
- Physician liaison

4. Develop an HIM Project Plan

The HIM project plan should reflect the following:

- Team members
- Objective
- WBS to reach the objective
- Team members responsible for each task within the WBS
- Timetable for meetings, milestones, and deliverables
- Identification of project methodology and communication tools

The HIM project team's objective is written and aligned with the organization's ICD-10 implementation steering committee's objective. Following is an example of an HIM objective:

> To transition our business organization's coded health information from ICD-9-CM to ICD-10-CM/PCS without interruption to the performance of the business functions reliant on coded data

The HIM project plan defines the objective, determines the WBS to achieve the objective, assigns responsibilities for the deliverables, and determines the timeline for completion. One of the most important components within the project plan is to determine how often to meet and how to communicate progress within the team and to the project steering committee. The communication plan must be determined at the beginning of the team's work so everyone knows his or her role in communicating issues and the team's progress toward the goal of the project. The communication plan will identify to who, what, and when information is to be delivered. There are many software application methods available and used by facilities today that make team collaboration and the ability to share project communication easier.

5. Create the Work Breakdown Structure

Create the WBS using nouns or verbs related to the HIM team's project plan deliverables. Many IS projects follow similar structure and breakdown, and a template an organization has previously developed may be used. If none is available, refer to table 1.1 (p. 9). It is important to keep the focus on the deliverable associated with each task in the WBS. For instance, an example of a task that could occur on the HIM team project plan is "assess contract coding vendor readiness." The deliverable for the task is the results of the findings obtained from the assessment, which is easily presented in spreadsheet or table format. All assignments of tasks are based on the responsible group participants' designated area of expertise. The participants should be committed to the project and actively contribute to the work of the project team. Understanding the importance of the task ranks, definitions, and expectations should be clearly defined and understood by each of the team participants before beginning the work to perform the task.

Although the HIM department team's plan for ICD-10-CM/PCS implementation will be closely aligned with the published date in the final rule, it is important to schedule the implementation plan early enough to successfully complete the tasks associated with meeting the objective before the published regulatory date.

Assessment of Educational Requirements for Coding Professionals

ACTION STEPS

1. Appoint a Coding Assessment Coordinator
2. Develop a Survey Questionnaire to Assess Educational Requirements in Each Department
3. Initiate an Education Process for Coding Professionals
4. Examine Staffing Needs
5. Evaluate the Coding Functions Across the Organization

During the assessment phase of the implementation, considerations in the preparation and assessment of the coding professionals in your facility will include surveying departments to understand where coding takes place (examples include admissions, radiology, pathology, and physician billing departments) and the education requirements for coding professionals in those departments.

1. Appoint a Coding Assessment Coordinator

The appointment of a coding assessment coordinator is essential to appraise baseline knowledge of all coding professionals in the organization, organize instruction, and collect information regarding coding activities for all facility departments where coding is performed. Developing a consistent education plan will alleviate staff concerns regarding the future changes and build confidence as well as ensure readiness of staff for Go-Live. Initially, the educational program should focus on understanding the following:

- Benefits and value of ICD-10-CM/PCS
- Regulatory process for adoption, anticipated implementation timeline, and variables affecting the timeline
- Structure, organization, and unique features of both ICD-10-CM and ICD-10-PCS (Bowman and Zeisset 2007).

Additionally, assessment of coders' proficiency in the biological sciences, such as anatomy and physiology, will be beneficial to prepare for necessary future educational needs (college courses, Webinars, and such).

2. Develop a Survey Questionnaire to Assess Educational Requirements in Each Department

A questionnaire to obtain information from each department within the facility regarding code generation and/or usage, as well as assessing educational needs of employees in each department, will need to include the following:

- Name of department
- Number of employees coding health data
- Number of employees using coded data
- Extent of codes used; for example, are codes used for multiple body systems or is coding limited to only one or two body systems?
- Use or source of historical coded data and specific timeframes for use of those data, for example, does the department use retrospective data? If so, how many years retrospectively is data

used? One to two years, three to five years, more than five years? And by whom?

- Would you participate in educational sessions with the HIM department?

Hospital departments tend to work very independently, and it is necessary for each clinical department to identify the ICD-10-CM/PCS education needs for its employees. Use the clinical department training plan template (figure 1.6) to list each clinical department employee who requires training and the level of training needed, and to identify any established and budgeted department training plans. Each clinical department could potentially have a patient registrant, a coding professional, and nursing professionals who would require different levels of ICD-10-CM/PCS knowledge. The educational requirement assessment should be done early in the implementation process to create ICD-10-CM/PCS awareness and to help the project steering committee identify the best method of delivery for training and education to the staff.

3. Initiate an Education Process for Coding Professionals

Education during the assessment phase of existing coding staff should be focused on learning the structure, organization, challenges, and unique features of ICD-10-CM/PCS. Approaching training in this manner will assist in application and understanding of the new code system, as well as to alleviate concerns and/or anxiety of the coding staff. One method may include practicing ICD-10-CM exercises using ICD-9-CM workbooks to apply ICD-10-CM codes during coding meetings once or twice during this phase. This is not the time for intense study as it is too far out from Go-Live, but exposure to the structure, unique qualities, and benefits will bolster coder confidence. Several publications and educational sessions through CMS and AHIMA are available on their respective Web sites. AHIMA also publishes Practice Briefs, ICD-10-CM/PCS educational materials such as *ICD-10-CM/PCS Preview*, and articles in the professional journal. Familiarize staff with Web sites to visit for information available on

Figure 1.6.   Clinical department training plan

Purpose
The purpose of the ICD-10-CM training plan is to: • Identify ICD-10-CM education and training needs in clinical departments • Plan for clinical department ICD-10-CM training events

Team Training Roles and Responsibilities

Role	Responsibilities
Project manager	• Developing training plan • Monitoring training events • Monitoring skill improvement
Project team	• Identifying training needs • Participating in training events
Sponsors	• Approving clinical department training plan

Team Training Needs

Name	Clinical Department	Training Needs	Training Plan
		What skills are needed?	What class? Where? When? Cost?

ICD-10-CM/PCS. Figures 1.7 and 1.8 suggest the four-year progression of a coding professional's ICD-10-CM/PCS training from assessment through implementation.

4. Examine Staffing Needs

While some organizations will have sufficient staff to perform all the necessary educational and quality monitoring functions, some organizations may require additional staffing to accommodate the above processes. Consideration of hiring new coding graduates at some point during the implementation phase may help to alleviate short-term coding backlogs as well as reallocating the facility's more experienced

Figure 1.7.   Health information coding professional four-year education plan for ICD-10-CM

ICD-10-CM			
Year 2009/2010	**Year 2011**	**Year 2012**	**Year 2013**
Expand/refresh knowledge in the biomedical sciences (anatomy and physiology, pathophysiology, pharmacology, and medical terminology)	Review ICD-10-CM coding guidelines and coding system differences	Guidelines application exercises with ICD-10-CM	Comprehensive education and training
Code structure and organization	ICD-10-CM implementation plan	Review disease category differences	Practice application to real cases in preparation for Go-Live
Benefits	ICD-10-CM implementation plan update	Practice applying codes to simple diagnostic statements	ICD-10-CM implementation plan update
Challenges		ICD-10-CM implementation plan update	
ICD-10-CM implementation plan update			

(continued on next page)

Figure 1.8.   Health information coding professional four-year education plan for ICD-10-PCS

	ICD-10-PCS			
2009/2010	**2011**	**2012**	**2013**	
Expand/refresh knowledge in the biomedical sciences (anatomy and physiology, pathophysiology, pharmacology, and medical terminology)	Learn ICD-10-PCS coding guidelines	Learn procedures in the ancillary sections	Comprehensive education and training	
ICD-10-PCS code structure and organization	Root operation groups	Practice applying codes with simple operative reports	Continue practice applying codes with operative reports	
Conventions used	Definitions of root operations and approaches	ICD-10-CM and PCS implementation plan update	ICD-10-CM and PCS implementation Go-Live plan	
ICD-10-PCS design	Begin review of procedures in the Medical and Surgical section			
ICD-10-PCS additional characteristics	List of Medical and Surgical-related sections of ICD-10-PCS			
ICD-10-PCS applications	Practice using coding exercises within the ICD-10-PCS coding reference manual or using other resources			
ICD-10- PCS implementation plan update	ICD-10-PCS implementation plan update			

coding professionals to educate and monitor quality. Facilities, to this point, have been somewhat reticent about hiring new coding graduates as it usually takes 12 to 18 months to completely familiarize new staff with coding guidelines and conventions and to become familiar with the unique facility culture and processes. At the point of Go-Live, all coders will have the same level of understanding of the ICD-10-CM and ICD-10-PCS coding systems. Facilities will have had the opportunity to educate both experienced professionals and the new coding graduates equally during the implementation phase. This allows facilities to have additional trained coding professionals in place at the time of implementation and frees up some of the long-term coding staff for ensuring data quality, reviewing coding accuracy, and for aggressively following up on outstanding account receivables due to inadequate documentation or other issues. The more experienced coding professionals also would have the opportunity to interact with the medical staff for documentation education and follow-up.

5. Evaluate the Coding Functions Across the Organization

If the coding function is being performed in many facility departments, consider if the facility is better served by consolidating the coding function into one department where education, coding quality, backlog, and account receivables are addressed in one concise process and staff team.

Adequate preparation of coding staff members and keeping them integrally involved and informed during implementation planning will facilitate a solid foundation for understanding ICD-10-CM/PCS. In addition, complete communication will contribute to building morale and allow for conversation to alleviate concerns during the implementation. Input from the coding group also will help to determine if resource allocation is required and gain insight into how to best minimize backlog to not overburden them.

Clinical Documentation Improvement Assessment

> **ACTION STEPS**
>
> 1. Assess Existing Documentation Practices
> 2. Conduct a Documentation Review
> 3. Review Physician Documentation Tools
> 4. Create ICD-10-CM/PCS Documentation Awareness

The facility plan for implementation of ICD-10-CM/PCS will require an early start in assessing all current clinical documentation practices. Accurate reporting and ICD-9-CM code assignment depends heavily upon physician and other provider clinical documentation. Over the years, healthcare and coding professional associations continue to focus on bridging the gap and stressing the importance of building a collaborative relationship between the coding professional and patient care providers. The national initiatives toward EHR implementation have greatly helped to improve the quality of content and legibility of clinical documentation relevant to patient encounters in all settings. Ongoing focus on value-based purchasing, quality reporting, regulatory development, and the implementation of ICD-10-CM/PCS will continue to require clinicians to be as specific as possible in documenting clinical observations pertaining to patient care and all patient visit encounter types.

1. Assess Existing Documentation Practices

During ICD-10-CM/PCS implementation planning, an assessment to determine the current level of specificity and quality of the physician clinical documentation practices should be performed. Many hospitals have initiated revenue improvement efforts for the inpatient encounter by establishing a documentation improvement or integrity department. Such a department usually consists of a team of nursing and coding specialists concurrently who review patient clinical documentation and perform real-time Medicare severity diagnosis-related group (MS-DRG) assignment as a predictor of encounter reimbursement. The exclusion of a code or assignment or a non-specific code may result in decreased reimbursement. Documentation specialists pose written or verbal queries to physicians to address any incomplete documentation of diagnoses or procedures, such as the linkages to corresponding terminology. Although some physician-specific documentation statistics—such as query rate and case-mix index—may be produced from a clinical documentation database, the result may reflect incomplete statistics regarding the lack of clinical documentation because all patient encounters are not captured for review.

2. Conduct a Documentation Review

In order to assess if clinical documentation practices are providing the detail needed for specific code assignment, the facility would benefit from an expert coding professional's review of a sample of records based on the highest volume MS-DRGs or a specific patient-type representing a high volume of the facilities healthcare consumers. For instance, a facility can analyze the frequency of nonspecific ICD-9-CM code assignments as principal diagnosis in the inpatient population for the cardiology department and compare the differences in physician clinical documentation detail needed for the same disease category in ICD-10-CM/PCS. The same method can be used for current outpatient testing services data to assess ordering diagnoses documentation based on specific service areas. As stated in 45 CFR 162:

> For some services, such as a particular drug or surgical procedure, there may be a National Coverage Decision (NCD) or a Local Coverage Decision (LCD) that requires the reporting of a list of specific diagnosis codes. These coverage decisions sometimes include unspecified codes but oftentimes they do not. In a handful of cases, the coverage decision will list several specific diagnosis codes needed

in order to make payments, and physicians are aware of the services or surgeries to which they apply. Under MS–DRGs, sometimes a lower payment results from reporting an unspecified code. An unspecified code will still result in a payment, but it might be a lower payment. The number of such cases will not necessarily increase as a result of the adoption of ICD-10.

Most likely, if coders are assigning nonspecific ICD-9-CM code ranges for reporting now, the same problem will persist once you begin to code with ICD-10-CM. Mapping the unspecified ICD-9-CM code report to ICD-10-CM code using the general equivalence mapping (GEM) files will help lead you to the more definitive character values, which may be assigned for the ICD-10-CM code range. Further analysis in reporting by service area or specific physicians may help focus education efforts to service areas identified as needing improvement.

3. Review Physician Documentation Tools

Assess any health information electronic documentation tools planned or currently used for physician documentation of procedural encounters that will include ICD-10-PCS detail. Begin a systematic review for code category detail of any clinical document templates used by physicians for history and physical, progress notes, consults, commonly performed inpatient procedures, and EHR smart text availability. Also assess disease-specific protocols that could provide an opportunity to enhance the clinical detail without jeopardizing the document integrity. If a facility is in the process of implementing an EHR, smart text access, drop-down menus, and checklists, as well as myriad other options, are designed to help physicians document conditions quickly and will help to accommodate needed specificity for ICD-10-CM/PCS code selection by service type. For example, this could include increased specificity of the information obtained in the physical exam portion on the electronic office visit encounter in a wound care management clinic before ICD-10-CM/PCS implementation. Increasing and improving specificity of the clinical documentation early in the process enhances the provider documentation to support and include the detail needed, for example, with ulcer coding in ICD-10-CM.

4. Create ICD-10-CM/PCS Documentation Awareness

Start early with an ICD-10-CM/PCS documentation awareness campaign. Some suggestions for clinical department talking points are included in appendix 1.3. Use physician newsletters or facility Web pages to focus on one service disease category at a time. Beginning with the highest volume service types or the least enhanced areas, highlight the specifics available once ICD-10-CM is implemented. Some diagnosis code areas within ICD-10-CM require documentation detail to support the most specific code. For example, neurology could be highlighted to show the detail that ICD-10-CM will include for epilepsy. The ICD-10-CM code range for epilepsy and recurrent seizures section, G40–G40.919, includes clinical documentation detail to assign the most specific code based on the condition stated as intractable or non-intractable, focal or generalized, idiopathic, or special epileptic syndromes related to alcohol, drugs, stress, and more. In addition, another significant change in ICD-10-CM/PCS is the inclusion of encounter and external injury cause details within the code selection.

Work to enhance physician documentation to include more accuracy in terminology, for example, stating "acute" or "chronic" when documenting active conditions instead of using "history of" for the conditions. This allows the coder to choose the most appropriate code in ICD-10-CM/PCS.

Facilities also will require a workflow analysis of the current post-discharge query process to prepare for any potential increase in queries that may occur during the transition to ICD-10-CM/PCS. An efficient postdischarge query process reduces delays in the facility revenue cycle, increases physician satisfaction, and provides valuable post–ICD-10-CM/PCS implementation educational direction for physicians.

References

45 CFR 162: HIPAA Administrative Simplification: Modifications to Medical Data Code Set Standards To Adopt ICD–10–CM and ICD–10–PCS. 2009 (Jan. 16).

Bowman, S. 2008. ICD-10 Preparation Checklist. *Journal of AHIMA* 79(3):32.

Bowman, S., and A. Zeisset. 2007. ICD-10 Preparation Checklist. *Journal of AHIMA* (online only).

Center for Medicare and Medicaid Services. ICD-10 Web site. http://www.cms.hhs.gov/ICD10/.

Talking Points for Senior Managers

How the Implementation of ICD-10-CM and ICD-10-PCS Will Affect Your Organization

OVERVIEW

The U.S. Department of Health and Human Services (HHS) has established a final rule to change the code sets to be used for reporting diagnoses and procedures on healthcare transactions. Code sets are collections of codes that are used to identify specific diagnoses and clinical procedures in claims and other transactions.

The International Classification of Diseases, ninth revision, Clinical Modification (ICD-9-CM) code set is currently used for reporting healthcare diagnoses and inpatient procedure codes in the United States.

Under the final rule, the ICD-9-CM code sets will be replaced with the International Classification of Diseases, 10ᵗʰ revision, Clinical Modification (ICD-10-CM) and International Classification of Diseases,

---

Disclaimer

This material was prepared as a service to the public and is not intended to grant rights or impose obligations. This publication may contain references or links to statutes, regulations, or other policy materials. The information provided is intended only to be a general summary. It is not intended to take the place of either the written law or regulations. We encourage readers to review the specific statutes, regulations, and other interpretive materials for a full and accurate statement of their contents.

10th revision, Procedural Classification System (ICD-10-PCS) code sets, effective October 1, 2013.

The transmission of ICD-10-CM/PCS codes requires the expanded functionality and format of X12 transaction standard Versions 5010 and D.0. A prerequisite to the ICD-10-CM/PCS implementation is the implementation of X12 5010 regulation, effective January 1, 2012. Both the ICD-10-CM/PCS and X12 5010 regulations were released simultaneously and can be found at the link below.

The final rules are available at http://www.cms.hhs.gov/Transaction CodeSetsStands/02_TransactionsandCodeSetsRegulations.asp

Who Uses Codes?

- All healthcare providers use diagnostic codes for conditions, symptoms, and diseases. In the future, ICD-10-CM will be used for diagnostic codes.
- Inpatient hospitals currently use ICD-9-CM (volume 3) for procedure coding. In the future, ICD-10-PCS will be used for inpatient hospital procedure coding.
- Provider visits and ambulatory and physician procedures are coded using Current Procedural Terminology (CPT®), which is owned by the American Medical Association. In the future, CPT will continue to be used for provider visits and ambulatory and physician procedures.

Processes Impacted

- MS-DRG conversion
- Conversion of other payment methodologies dependent on diagnosis/procedure codes
- National and local coverage determinations
- System logic and edits (for example, medical necessity)
- Provider profiling
- Quality measurement and quality initiatives
- Claims editing

- Claims data analysis
- Utilization management
- Disease management
- Aggregate data reporting

Systems Impacted

- Modified field lengths to accommodate expanded data element length
- Modified logic to accommodate the ICD-10-CM and ICD-10-PCS code sets
- Systems accommodate the transmission of ICD-9-CM, ICD-10-CM, and ICD-10-PCS simultaneously
- Data-reporting elements
- Payment/revenue cycle systems changes
- Coding software systems
- End-coder software systems
- Physician technology (handhelds, etc.)

Operational Impacts

- Clinical documentation training
- Plan for ICD-10-CM and ICD-10-PCS training for all impacted staff
- Decreased coding and payment productivity post Go-Live

Financial Impacts

- Decreased revenue initially
- Altered revenue payment due to mapping of ICD-9-CM codes to ICD-10-CM and ICD-10-PCS for DRG and payment classification
- Increased payment error rate post Go-Live

Prepare for Implementation

- Begin discussion of ICD-10 now to facilitate early awareness and education—take advantage of lead time.
- Perform detailed impact analysis, including systems inventory and current use of ICD-9-CM codes

- Create a task force with all key departments represented to facilitate change and information dissemination
- Assess impact and training needs for physician, clinician, nursing, and ancillary department education
- Gather departmental information to assess implementation risks

ICD-10 Resources

- AHIMA's ICD-10 Web site
  http://www.ahima.org/icd10/
- The final rule
  http://edocket.access.gpo.gov/2009/pdf/E9-743.pdf
- General ICD-10-CM Information
  http://www.cms.hhs.gov/ICD10/
- Fact Sheet: HHS Modifies HIPAA Code Sets (ICD-10) and Electronic Transactions Standards
  http://www.cms.hhs.gov/apps/media/fact_sheets.asp
- To read the HHS press release issued on ICD-10:
  http://www.hhs.gov/news/press/2008pres/2008.html
- January 2009 Release of ICD-10-CM, which includes preface, index, tabular list, table of drugs and chemicals, and general equivalence mapping (GEM) files
  http://www.cdc.gov/nchs/about/otheract/icd9/abticd10.htm

Frequently Asked Questions

What type of testing has been done on ICD-10-CM and ICD-10-PCS?

Both systems have undergone formal testing. CMS conducted a formal test of ICD-10-PCS using CMS Contractor, Clinical Data Abstraction Centers (CDACs). Formal testing of ICD-10-CM has been conducted by the CDACs, American Hospital Association (AHA), and American Health Information Management Association (AHIMA). The 2003 report is available at http://www.ahima.org/icd10/documents/FinalStudy_000.pdf

Is ICD-10-CM mainly intended for hospital inpatient coding?

No, ICD-10-CM will replace ICD-9-CM diagnosis codes and will be used for reporting all diagnoses regardless of setting.

Will the increased number of ICD-10-CM diagnoses codes lead to an increase in ambulatory care payments?

No, ambulatory care payments are based on CPT and alpha-numeric HCPCS codes. The increased number of ICD-10-CM diagnoses will not lead to more ambulatory care claims. The provider will continue to submit bills for services using CPT and alpha-numeric HCPCS codes. The patient's condition, symptoms, or diagnoses will be described using ICD-10-CM instead of ICD-9-CM. While there are significantly more ICD-10-CM codes than there are ICD-9-CM diagnosis codes, it is not anticipated that it will take more ICD-10-CM codes, on average, to describe the patient's condition. The reported codes will simply provide more precise information, which will improve the ability to better evaluate the type and cost of services used for a specific diagnosis.

What can organizations do now to prepare for implementation of ICD-10-CM/PCS?

- Identify stakeholders
- Assess impact
- Formulate strategies and identify goals
- Develop education and training plans for employees at all levels
- Develop information systems and technology systems change implementation plan

Additional ICD-10-CM/PCS frequently asked questions are available at:

http://www.cms.hhs.gov/ICD10/01_Overview.asp

Talking Points for Information Systems Managers

How the Implementation of ICD-10-CM/PCS Will Affect the Information Systems Inventory

OVERVIEW

The U.S. Department of Health and Human Services (HHS) has established a final rule to change the code sets to be used for reporting diagnoses and procedures on healthcare transactions. Code sets are collections of codes that are used to identify specific diagnoses and clinical procedures in claims and other transactions.

The International Classification of Diseases, ninth revision, Clinical Modification (ICD-9-CM) code set is currently used for reporting healthcare diagnoses and inpatient procedure codes in the United States.

Under the final rule, the ICD-9-CM code sets will be replaced with the International Classification of Diseases, 10th revision, Clinical Modification (ICD-10-CM) and International Classification of Diseases,

---

Disclaimer

This material was prepared as a service to the public and is not intended to grant rights or impose obligations. This publication may contain references or links to statutes, regulations, or other policy materials. The information provided is intended only to be a general summary. It is not intended to take the place of either the written law or regulations. We encourage readers to review the specific statutes, regulations, and other interpretive materials for a full and accurate statement of their contents.

10th revision, Procedural Classification System (ICD-10-PCS) code sets, effective October 1, 2013.

The transmission of ICD-10-CM/PCS codes requires the expanded functionality and format of X12 transaction standard Versions 5010 and D.0. A prerequisite to the ICD-10-CM/PCS implementation is the implementation of X12 5010 regulation, effective January 1, 2012. Both the ICD-10-CM/PCS and X12 5010 regulations were released simultaneously and can be found at the link below.

The final rules are available at http://www.cms.hhs.gov/ TransactionCodeSetsStands/02_TransactionsandCodeSets Regulations.asp

Who Uses Codes?

- All healthcare providers will use ICD-10-CM diagnostic codes.
- Inpatient hospitals currently use ICD-9-CM (volume 3) for procedure coding. In the future, ICD-10-PCS will be used for inpatient hospital procedure coding.
- Provider visits and ambulatory and physician procedures are coded using Current Procedural Terminology (CPT®), which will continue to be used for provider visits and ambulatory and physician procedures.

Code Characteristics

ICD-9	ICD-10
Diagnosis Codes	
ICD-9-CM has 3–5 digits The first digit is numeric or alpha (E or V) Digits 2–5 are numeric	ICD-10-CM has 3–7 digits Digit 1 is alpha Digit 2 & 3 are numeric Digits 4–7 are alpha or numeric
Procedure Codes	
ICD-9-CM has 3–4 digits All digits are numeric	ICD-10-PCS has 7 digits Each can be either alpha or numeric

Impact on Systems

- Upgraded software to accommodate expanded field lengths and code changes
- Modified system field lengths to accommodate expanded data element length
- Modified system logic to accommodate the ICD-10-CM and ICD-10-PCS code sets
- Systems must accommodate the transmission of ICD-9-CM, ICD-10-CM, and ICD-10-PCS simultaneously
- Update superbills/encounter forms and databases
- Retain access to historical coded data in ICD-9-CM format
- Review of storage and reporting practices for longitudinal data
- Payment/revenue cycle systems changes
- Coding software systems
- End-coder software systems
- Physician technology (handhelds, etc.)

Other System Modifications to Consider

- Implementation of 5010 is a *prerequisite* to the implementation of ICD-10-CM/PCS
- Implementation of HIPAA X12 Version 5010
- Implementation of Version D.0
  —Covered entities must comply with Version 5010 and Version D.0 on January 1, 2012
- Implementation of Version 3.0
  —Covered entities must comply with the standard for Medicaid pharmacy subrogation transactions Version 3.0 on January 1, 2012
  —Small health plans have an additional year to comply with Version 3.0, due by January 1, 2013

Processes Impacted

- MS-DRG conversion
- Conversion of other payment methodologies dependent on diagnosis/procedure codes

- National and local coverage determinations
- System logic and edits (for example, medical necessity)
- Provider profiling
- Quality measurement and quality initiatives
- Claims editing
- Claims data analysis
- Utilization management
- Disease management
- Aggregate data reporting

Prepare for Implementation

- Begin discussion of ICD-10 now to facilitate early awareness and education—take advantage of lead time.
- Perform detailed impact analysis, including systems inventory and current use of ICD-9-CM codes
- Create a task force with all key departments represented to facilitate change and information dissemination
- Assess impact and training needs for physician, clinician, nursing, and ancillary department education
- Gather departmental information to assess implementation risks

ICD-10 Resources

- AHIMA's ICD-10 Web site
  http://www.ahima.org/icd10/
- The final rule
  http://edocket.access.gpo.gov/2009/pdf/E9-743.pdf
- General ICD-10-CM Information
  http://www.cms.hhs.gov/ICD10/
- Fact Sheet: HHS Modifies HIPAA Code Sets (ICD-10) and Electronic Transactions Standards
  http://www.cms.hhs.gov/apps/media/fact_sheets.asp
- To read the HHS press release issued on ICD-10:
  http://www.hhs.gov/news/press/2008pres/2008.html

■ January 2009 Release of ICD-10-CM, which includes preface, index, tabular list, table of drugs and chemicals, and general equivalence mapping (GEM) files

http://www.cdc.gov/nchs/about/otheract/icd9/abticd10.htm

Frequently Asked Questions

What type of testing has been done on ICD-10-CM and ICD-10-PCS?

Both systems have undergone formal testing. CMS conducted a formal test of ICD-10-PCS, using CMS Contractor, Clinical Data Abstraction Centers (CDACs). Formal testing of ICD-10-CM has been conducted by the CDACs, American Hospital Association (AHA), and American Health Information Management Association (AHIMA). The 2003 report is available at http://www.ahima.org/icd10/documents/FinalStudy_000.pdf

Is ICD-10-CM mainly intended for hospital inpatient coding?

No, ICD-10-CM will replace ICD-9-CM diagnosis codes and will be used for reporting all diagnoses regardless of setting.

Will the increased number of ICD-10-CM diagnoses codes lead to an increase in ambulatory care payments?

No, ambulatory care payments are based on CPT and alpha-numeric HCPCS codes. The increased number of ICD-10-CM diagnosis will not lead to more ambulatory care claims. The provider will continue to submit bills for services using CPT and alpha-numeric HCPCS codes. The patient's condition, symptoms, or diagnoses will be described using ICD-10-CM instead of ICD-9-CM. While there are significantly more ICD-10-CM codes than there are ICD-9-CM diagnosis codes, it is not anticipated that it will take more ICD-10-CM codes, on average, to describe the patient's condition. The reported codes will simply provide more precise information, which will improve the ability to better evaluate the type and cost of services used for a specific diagnosis.

What can organizations do now to prepare for implementation of ICD-10-CM/PCS?

- Identify stakeholders
- Assess impact
- Formulate strategies and identify goals
- Develop education/training plans for employees at all levels
- Develop information systems/technology systems change implementation plan

Additional ICD-10-CM/PCS frequently asked questions are available at:

http://www.cms.hhs.gov/ICD10/01_Overview.asp

Talking Points for Clinical Department Managers

How ICD-10 Will Affect You as a Clinical Department Manager

OVERVIEW

The U.S. Department of Health and Human Services (HHS) has established a final rule to change the code sets to be used for reporting diagnoses and procedures on healthcare transactions. Code sets are collections of codes that are used to identify specific diagnoses and clinical procedures in claims and other transactions.

The International Classification of Diseases, ninth revision, Clinical Modification (ICD-9-CM) code set is currently used for reporting healthcare diagnoses and inpatient procedure codes in the United States.

Under the final rule, the ICD-9-CM code sets will be replaced with the International Classification of Diseases, 10th revision, Clinical Modification (ICD-10-CM) and International Classification of Diseases,

---

Disclaimer

This material was prepared as a service to the public and is not intended to grant rights or impose obligations. This publication may contain references or links to statutes, regulations, or other policy materials. The information provided is intended only to be a general summary. It is not intended to take the place of either the written law or regulations. We encourage readers to review the specific statutes, regulations, and other interpretive materials for a full and accurate statement of their contents.

10th revision, Procedural Classification System (ICD-10-PCS) code sets, effective October 1, 2013.

The final rules are available at http://www.cms.hhs.gov/ TransactionCodeSetsStands/02_TransactionsandCodeSets Regulations.asp

Who Uses Codes?

- All healthcare providers use diagnostic codes for conditions, symptoms, and diseases. In the future, ICD-10-CM will be used for diagnostic codes.
- Inpatient hospitals currently use ICD-9-CM (volume 3) for procedure coding. In the future, ICD-10-PCS will be used for inpatient hospital procedure coding.
- Provider visits and ambulatory and physician procedures are coded using Current Procedural Terminology (CPT®), which is owned by the American Medical Association. In the future, CPT will continue to be used for provider visits and ambulatory and physician procedures.

ICD-10-CM Changes

- Alphanumeric—three to seven characters
- Specificity and detail significantly expanded
- ICD-10-CM has approximately 55,000 more codes than ICD-9-CM diagnosis codes
- More codes does not mean more complicated

ICD-10-PCS Changes

- Seven character alphanumeric
- Each character has a consistent meaning throughout the code set
- Root operation definitions specifies the objective of a procedure
- ICD-10-PCS helps identify new technologies and medical procedures

■ Greater specificity in procedure codes for research and utilization statistics

ICD-10-CM Benefits

■ Descriptive, robust categories for more precise coding; streamlined reimbursement processes; richer quality data; and treatment planning

■ Maximizes value of clinical data and benefits of interoperable electronic health records system

■ Greater detail for patient and physician profiles

■ Greater detail for quality reporting

■ Enhanced monitoring of resource utilization

■ Improving clinical, financial, and administrative performance measurement

■ Expanded capability to prevent and detect healthcare fraud and abuse

■ Tracking public health risks

ICD-10-CM New Features

■ Combination codes for conditions and common disease symptoms or manifestations

■ Combination codes for poisonings and external causes

■ Injury, external cause, and fracture extensions showing episode of care

■ Expanded codes (injury, diabetes, alcohol/substance abuse, postoperative complications)

■ Added laterality

■ Increased specificity

■ Full code titles are used in ICD-10-CM

Examples of added laterality in ICD-10:

■ C50.512 Malignant neoplasm of lower-outer quadrant of left female breast

■ H02.041 Spastic entropion of right upper eyelid

■ M05.771 Rheumatoid arthritis with rheumatoid factor of right ankle and foot without organ or systems involvement

ICD-10-CM has combination codes for conditions and common symptoms or manifestations.

Examples include:

- I25.110 Atherosclerotic heart disease of native coronary artery with unstable angina
- K71.51 Toxic liver disease with chronic active hepatitis with ascites
- K50.012 Crohn's disease of small intestine with intestinal obstruction
- N13.731 Vesicoureteral-reflux with reflux nephropathy with hydroureter, unilateral

ICD-10–CM has combination codes for poisonings and external causes.

Examples include:

- T48.4x5A Adverse effect of expectorants, initial encounter
- T48.6x1D Poisoning by antiasthmatics, accidental (unintentional), subsequent encounter
- T46.4x6A Underdosing of angiotensin–converting–enzyme inhibitors, initial encounter
- T43.6x2S Poisoning by psychostimulants with abuse potential, intentional self–harm, sequelae

Impact of Conversion to ICD-10-CM

Challenges

- Clinical documentation will need greater specificity
- Revenue system and database changes
- Potential workflow process changes
- Department staff education

Benefits

- Codes are specific to type of complication and in some cases linked to specific procedures
- Ability to use specific coded data for Present on Admission (POA) and Potentially Preventable Events (PPE) determinations in future payment to healthcare providers

- Greater specificity for pay-for-performance programs and medical necessity
- Greater detail for creating disease management and utilization protocols

Conversion

- Plan for ICD-10-CM training for all impacted department staff
- Work with vendors to obtain upgraded software to accommodate expanded field lengths and code changes
- Check CMS Medicare Learning Network for changes in Coverage policies
- Update superbills, patient encounter forms, EHR, and registration databases
- Retain access to historical coded data
- System field lengths must be expanded to accommodate expanded data element length
- Understand the impact to payment systems and assess impact of those changes
- Determination of impacts on facility revenue cycle
- Review of storage and reporting practices for longitudinal data
- Impact and training needs assessments for physicians, clinicians, nursing, and ancillary department education
- Staff awareness plan
- Clinical documentation analysis and training
- Impact assessment on staff and physician technology (hand-helds, etc.)

Process

- Department staff training assessment
- Increased clinical documentation needs
- Patient registration for the department processes
- Advanced beneficiary notice department processes
- Reporting needs for departments utilizing coded data
- National and local coverage determinations

- System logic and edits (for example, medical necessity)
- Provider profiling
- Quality measurement and quality initiatives reporting
- Claims editing
- Claims data analysis
- Utilization management
- Disease management
- Aggregate data reporting

Frequently Asked Questions

Is ICD-10-CM mainly intended for hospital inpatient coding?

No, ICD-10-CM will replace ICD-9-CM diagnosis codes and will be used for reporting all diagnoses regardless of setting.

Will the increased number of ICD-10-CM diagnoses codes lead to an increase in the number of physician bills?

No, physicians will continue to be paid based on CPT and HCPCS codes. They will capture diagnoses on their bills using ICD-10-CM. The increased specificity in the ICD-10-CM code may lead to a reduction in bills that are returned for additional information. For instance, when patients sought evaluation and care because of possible exposure to anthrax, there was no ICD-9-CM code to clearly indicate the reason for the encounter. It was only after the creation of new and specific anthrax codes that we were able to track encounters and outcomes using a precise diagnosis code. Precise diagnosis codes provide more information about the service. They do not lead to additional bills or payment.

What can organizations do now to prepare for implementation of ICD-10-CM/PCS?

- Identify stakeholders
- Assess impact to every department

- Formulate strategies and identify goals
- Develop education and training plans for employees at all levels
- Develop information systems and technology systems change implementation plan

ICD-10 Resources

- AHIMA's ICD-10 Web site
  http://www.ahima.org/icd10/
- General ICD-10-CM Information
  http://www.cms.hhs.gov/ICD10/
- Fact Sheet: HHS Modifies HIPAA Code Sets (ICD-10) and Electronic Transactions Standards
  http://www.cms.hhs.gov/apps/media/fact_sheets.asp
- To read the HHS press release issued on ICD-10:
  http://www.hhs.gov/news/press/2008pres/2008.html
- January 2009 Release of ICD-10-CM, which includes preface, index, tabular list, table of drugs and chemicals, and general equivalence mapping (GEM) files
  http://www.cdc.gov/nchs/about/otheract/icd9/abticd10.htm

Overall Implementation

The assessment activities provided you with information necessary to determine the amount of work as well as funding required to complete the necessary modifications organization-wide. Based on the findings, the implementation plan, schedule, and budget can be updated. This chapter will walk through the process to complete the activities necessary to modify systems, update processes, and educate the facility's resources in preparation for the ICD-10-CM/PCS Go-Live.

Organization-wide Implementation Plan

ACTION STEPS

1. Identify and Rank Organizational Risks
2. Complete a Gap Analysis
3. Update Implementation Plans and Schedule
4. Update Project Resources
5. Update Project Budget

1. Identify and Rank Organizational Risks

Now that you have completed an assessment, the project team should review the findings (answers to the assessment questions), identify, and rank organizational risks. The risk ranking will provide the organization with a list of impact areas that should be focused on first versus those areas that can wait until a later date to be addressed. The risk ranking will also provide the organization with information to develop an overall strategy for conducting process and systems modification, testing, and Go-Live activities. The risk assessment template shown in figure 2.1 displays the regulatory ranking components, and each impact area has its own ranking component.

Figure 2.1. Risk assessment template

Strategic Category	Strategic Component[1]	Risk Description[2]	Probability[3]
Technology (Software)			
	Admissions/Scheduling		
	EMR/EHR/Coding Software		
	Encoding Application		
	DRG Grouper		
	Billing Software		
	Payment Management Software		
	Research		
	Auditing		
	Lab System		
	Pharmacy System		
	Clinical System		
	Cancer Registry System		
	Report Database/Server		
	Additional		
People			
	Accounting/Finance Staff		
	Admitting Staff		
	Clinical Staff		
	Coding Staff		
	Contractors		
	HIM Staff		
	IT Staff		
	Operations Management		
	Patient/Outreach		
	Software Developers		
	Sr. Management		
	Additional		
Processes			
	Accounting/Finance		
	Admitting		
	Case Review		
	Claims Processing		
	Clinical Operation		
	Coding		
	Communication		
	Discharge		
	HIM Operations		
	IT Support		
	Marketing		
	Operations Management		
	Patient/Outreach		
	Reporting		
	Sr. Management		
	Training		
	Additional		

Figure 2.1. Risk assessment template *(continued)*

Impact[4]	Score[5]	Event (Trigger)[6]	Response[7]	Contingency Plan[8]	Resources[9]	Lead[10]
SUM						

SUM						

SUM RISK SCORE						

continued on next page

Figure 2.1.   **Risk assessment template** *(continued)*

	Probability
4	Highly likely/probable (76%-100%)
3	Likely (51%-75%)
2	Somewhat likely (26%-50%)
1	Unlikely/improbable (0%-25%)

	Impact
40	Critical: Stops multiple daily operations/functions. No workaround.
30	Severe: Reduces daily operations/functions. Workaround exists but cannot sustain option for longer than 14 days.
20	Moderate: Delays daily operations/functions with out stoppage. Long-term workaround exists.
10	Minimal: No significant impact; however, may increase project costs.

Risk Score
Critical: 161 - 320
Severe: 121 - 160
Moderate: 79 - 120
Minimal: 10 - 78

Figure 2.1.   Risk assessment template *(continued)*

[1] Modify this list to meet your organization's needs. Be as specific as possible to cover all areas of risk.

[2] Brief description of the risk for each strategic category.

[3] See scale.

[4] See scale.

[5] Total risk score for each strategic component and strategic category.

[6] Brief description of when/how this risk will occur.

[7] Brief description of what the organization will do in response: Avoid, transfer, mitigate, or accept.

[8] Brief description of a plan to respond to the risk, such as backup or workaround.

[9] Who will work on the risk response and contingency plan.

[10] Who will lead the response.

The assessment findings, as well as the format of the ICD-10-CM/PCS and 5010 and regulation requirements, will enable each organization to develop a gap analysis between the current and future environments. Project leadership should review the assessment findings, calculate the risk ranking, and enter the values into the risk assessment worksheet. The risk ranking process first identifies all the strategic categories responsible for critical functions within an organization and is impacted by the ICD-10-CM/PCS implementation. Strategic components are then added under the strategic categories. Strategic components are the specific department, areas, or function affected by the identified strategic categories. The project team should then review the list of strategic components and complete the following steps:

1. Detail a description of the risk.
2. Identify the probability of the risk occurring (rank 1 to 4 with 4 being most likely).
3. Identify the impact if the risk were to occur (rank 10, 20, 30 or 40 with 40 being the most significant impact). Column will change color based on score value.
4. Review score value balance to identify the overall ranking of risks for your organization.
5. Document the trigger for the risk event to occur or not occur depending on the risk.
6. Document the response to the risk event.
7. Document a brief contingency plan should the risk occur.
8. Identify resources required to participate in the contingency plan.
9. Identify a resource responsible to lead the team included in the contingency plan.

The risk assessment template included in the CD-ROM can be customized by your organization. The color of the worksheet cells changes; the critical impact (highest priority/highest risk) scores turn red, severe impact (medium priority) scores turn orange, moderate impact (moderate priority) scores turn yellow, and minimal impact (low priority) scores turn green. (The CD contains a similar item, the Readiness Assessment Tool, that may also be used.) The following steps detail how to complete a risk assessment process:

1. Complete the impact assessment process.
2. Complete the risk assessment worksheet.
3. Identify organizational strategic priority categories based on the highest ranked risks areas from the worksheet results.
4. Integrate the risk assessment findings with the ICD-10 action plan milestones.
5. Prioritize milestones according to strategic priorities.
6. Review/discuss priorities and communicate to organizational executives.

Upon completion of the risk ranking process, the steering committee should first revisit the initial organization-wide project strategy and make any necessary adjustments on resources or operations to focus on the highest areas of risk, followed by subsequent areas according to the ranking scores. Data from the review process activities may also require updates to the project schedule and budget.

2. Complete a Gap Analysis

In order to identify all specific tasks necessary to complete the 5010 and ICD-10-CM/PCS implementation specific to your organization, an organization-wide gap analysis needs to be completed. The gap analysis will assess the differences between the current and future (desired) use of ICD-9-CM codes within software systems, operational workflows, and coding knowledge within your organization compared to what will be required to comply with the final rules of ICD-10-CM/PCS as well as 5010. Gaps are identified as areas requiring modification, either to a system, process, or function. Flow charts (gap maps) may need to be developed to identify current and future state differences as a means to document areas where alterations are required. The risk assessment provides the project team with the order to complete the gap assessment activities; however, it does not eliminate the need for areas of low or minimal impact to complete the gap assessment process. The detailed gap assessment process requires knowledgeable resources to identify specific steps required to transition systems, operations, and resource knowledge from the current state to the required future state. Future state design, workflow, or configuration of software systems and outsourced operations will also require interaction with vendors and contractors responsible for the associated system or function. The result of the gap assessment will provide the organization with a comprehensive understanding of tasks and associated steps required to transition to 5010 as well as to ICD-10-CM/PCS. Once the gap assessment activities are completed, the organization resources can begin the work of the project, including the modification testing and deployment of new systems, processes, and operations.

3. Update Implementation Plans and Schedule

The next step is to work with the appropriate resources, both internally and externally, to update the work (tasks, duration, resource, and budget requirements) to complete the required modifications to systems, processes, and resources (people). Based on the tasks with the longest duration, typically including software modifications, the project schedule can be updated with more realistic estimates. The implementation deadlines for both the ICD-10-CM/PCS and 5010 regulations provide healthcare organizations with end dates or Go-Live dates that mandate when the modifications need to be completed. The final regulations suggest getting started in 2009 with system inventory and assessment activities in preparation for the 5010 modification requirements, which are the foundation of the ICD-10-CM/PCS code set implementation. The system modifications required for the 5010 regulation are extensive; however, the specifics are outside of this book's scope. Each organization should conduct research to adequately assess the impact and readiness to accommodate the 5010 regulation.

4. Update Project Resources

As the project tasks are being updated and detailed tasks are being identified, the appropriate resources should also be assigned to new tasks. As well, resources should be evaluated for preliminarily assigned tasks. The key project roles were discussed in the first chapter, which included members of various departments. A project of this magnitude will require many resources to complete each task within the overall plan. Identifying many resources up front in the project will assist the project team members with coordinating their efforts and completing their tasks according to the schedule timelines. As the project timeline progresses, it is important to appropriately identify the resources requirements and commitments allocated to completing each task. In addition, it is equally important for each project resource to acknowledge the commitment of the project work. Tasks identified as part of the critical path will have a direct impact on the overall project success and should be accounted for accordingly by all project team members. If one resource is not enough to complete a specific task, adjustments to the project schedule and resource requirements should be made.

5. Update Project Budget

The process of developing an accurate project budget is extremely important, as a project of this size with multiple variables easily can get out of control and negatively impact the organization as a whole. The results of the assessment activities will provide updates to the initial project budget estimates. The updated estimates should be subjected to the steering committee's approval in the same process the initial documents experienced. Once the updated budget has been approved, the project manager should identify a resource to manage the budget. Depending on the available resources within your organization, you may be able to devote specific resources to assist with developing and monitoring the project budget. If this option is not reasonable, organize a team and develop a process to manage the budgeting activities through the responsibility of multiple resources. The budgeting process can be cumbersome for an individual resource not devoted to the position; therefore, your organization may prefer to implement a budgeting committee on the project to accommodate the workload requirements.

Information Systems Implementation Process

1. Review Assessment Findings
2. Negotiate Contracts and Addendums
3. Update Budget and Resource Estimates
4. Update Work Plan

Software applications within each facility will be directly impacted by the implementation of the HIPAA transaction updates as well as the use of the ICD-10-CM/PCS code sets. Current systems were evaluated during the assessment process and identified modifications required to comply with the regulations were documented. As a result, some systems most likely were identified as not being able to meet the new standards.

1. Review Assessment Findings

The findings collected during the detailed analysis of each system impacted by the transition to ICD-10-CM/PCS and the 5010 transactions should have included estimates regarding the level of effort and budget considerations required to complete the modifications. Replies to the survey questions should be reviewed in detail to determine the level of impact as well as requirements necessary to accommodate the regulations. In some cases, the findings will discover software systems that are incompatible with the updated standards, either due to their current configuration or because the cost to modify the system is greater than the cost to acquire and implement a replacement system, such as legacy financial and claims data systems.

Collection of the assessment findings will be used to complete a detailed Gap Analysis of all software systems. Findings will most likely provide the IS department with more information regarding the current systems functionality throughout your organization. Although it is labor-intensive, diagramming future processes for all software systems impacted by the 5010 and ICD-10-CM/PCS implementations will benefit an organization in the long-term and become a baseline when implemented. As the implementation process continues to update, test, and validate systems, resources will identify opportunities to employ best practices and update policy and procedures. The regulatory mandates are extensive and require organizations to make change; now is the time to take advantage of the work being done and to change all the areas having opportunities to improve efficiency and productivity.

Gap analysis activities may require project team members to conduct multiple interviews with individual contractors, vendors, or system engineers to adequately understand the requirements necessary to modify the technology systems. Follow-up activities can be time consuming if not well thought out before conducting the interviews. Most likely, the resources required to answer the pertinent questions will be difficult to schedule; therefore, prior planning and preparation for these interviews is important not only to keep the project on schedule but also out of consideration for the interviewees. The need to modify systems within a specified timeframe (in order to meet the regulation timelines) most likely will include some aspect of negotiation regarding finances with the various software vendors and contractors. Software modifications are critical to the submission of claims data and thus reimbursement for each organization; therefore, every organization should have a vested interest in ensuring that modifications to systems are completed and adequately tested in accordance to the project schedule.

2. Negotiate Contracts and Addendums

Software vendors and contractors have a variety of ways to update their systems, including routine releases to current platforms, custom modifications, and new platform releases. It is important to know if modifications to systems are included in a current maintenance contract or if the modifications will require a contract addendum from each software vendor. Negotiating with a current vendor on system modifications is typically timelier than the process to acquire and implement a replacement system; however, every vendor is different and will need to be handled individually. Plan to spend the most amount of time on software systems that are incompatible with the new regulations (legacy systems). Early detection of applications and software systems that need to be replaced will provide your organization with the most amount of time to complete all the phases of acquiring and implementing a new technology.

3. Update Budget and Resource Estimates

Software modifications will require the most significant amount of resources for the entire project, including staff time, process improvement, and education expenses. The initial budget estimate will need to be updated to encompass the estimates provided to your organization by all associated vendors and contractors. Including contingency and reserve estimates in the project budget is essential to staying within your target limits on this type of project. Software implementation and modification costs can vary by vendor and may include fixed-fee, cost-plus, or time and materials contracts. A variety of contracts can easily add unforeseen expenses to an unmanaged budget. The resource(s) assigned to manage the project budget will greatly assist the project manager when it comes to keeping a handle on the budget and tracking vendor expenses. Each software vendor and contractor required to accommodate software systems should be required to provide your organization with the following information:

- Scope of work required to complete the modifications
- Milestones required to complete the project work
- Time estimate for each milestone
- Vendor/contractor resource cost for each milestone
- Requirements for your organization to complete during project
- Contract type (fixed fee, cost plus, time and materials, etc.)
- Terms of contract (payment terms)

The CD-ROM includes a budget estimate worksheet that will assist you with developing a budget for your project (Project Budget Planning Excel worksheet). An extract of this tool is shown in figure 2.2. Each organization should determine the amount of contingency and back-up funds required for the project and include that total in the overall project budget. A typical budget estimate includes a 10 percent contingency and a 5 to 20 percent reserve budget depending on the identified risks for each software system. The use of the contingent and reserve funds should be limited, and their use should be controlled through a formal approval process and vote by the project steering committee.

4. Update Work Plan

Once you have completed the contract negotiations, you can determine the final project work plan, including timelines and schedule for completing the work to modify each software system within your organization. An example of a system modification timeline is shown in figure 2.3.

The system modification timeline will provide the project team with information to update the baseline project schedule. Review of the initial project work plan may reveal that some identified tasks are no longer relevant to the work required for your organization. The IS project lead should work with the project manager to update the project work breakdown structure to ensure that all necessary tasks have been included in the schedule and all staff have been identified and made available for the project. It may be necessary for additional support to be added to the project team if the activities required are beyond the scope of internal resources. The tools required for completing the project work should also be finalized by the IS and HIM teams and presented to the project manager in this phase. The project manager will incorporate all the IS and HIM updates and requirements into the final project schedule and supporting plans to present to the steering committee for approval. Once the final schedule, staffing, and plans have been approved, the project manager can distribute

Figure 2.2. Extract of budget estimate worksheet

Project Information

Project Manager	
Budget Manager	
Project Sponsor	
Project Start Date	mm/dd/yyyy
Last Modified Date	mm/dd/yyyy

Planned Budget Details To Date

	Vendor List			
Vendor Expense Types	Vendor A	Vendor B	Vendor C	Vendor D
License Fees	$ -	$ -	$ -	$ -
Consulting Services Fees	$ -	$ -	$ -	$ -
Development Fees	$ -	$ -	$ -	$ -
Maintenance Fees	$ -	$ -	$ -	$ -
Additional Fees	$ -	$ -	$ -	$ -
Total Vendor Fees	$ -	$ -	$ -	$ -

Figure 2.2. Extract of budget estimate worksheet (*continued*)

Contractor List

Contractor Expense Types	Contractor A	Contractor B	Contractor C	Contractor D
Consulting Services Fees	$ –	$ –	$ –	$ –
Development Fees	$ –	$ –	$ –	$ –
Additional Fees	$ –	$ –	$ –	$ –
Total Contractor Fees	$ –	$ –	$ –	$ –

Training Expense List

Training Expense Type	Department A	Department B	Department C	Department D
Coding Education	$ –	$ –	$ –	$ –
Software Education	$ –	$ –	$ –	$ –
Process Improvement	$ –	$ –	$ –	$ –
Change Management	$ –	$ –	$ –	$ –
Additional Training	$ –	$ –	$ –	$ –
Total Training Expense Types	$ –	$ –	$ –	$ –

Total Expenses	
Vendor	$ –
Contractor	$ –
Training	$ –
Grand Total Budget	$ –

Figure 2.3.   Sample system modification timeline

ID	Task Name	Start	Finish
1	Initial Systems Inventory	1/5/2009	6/4/2009
2	Conduct IT Systems Assessment	6/5/2009	9/9/2009
3	Review Assessment Findings (GAP Analysis)	9/10/2009	1/12/2010
4	Systems Modifications Identified	1/1/2010	1/1/2010
5	Vendor A – Contract Negociations	1/13/2010	7/1/2010
6	Vendor A – Complete System Modifications	7/2/2010	3/2/2011
7	Vendor A – System Modifications Testing	3/3/2011	6/1/2011
8	Vendor B – Contract Negotiations	1/1/2010	5/12/2010
9	Vendor B – Complete System Modifications	5/13/2010	9/13/2010
10	Vendor B – System Modification Testing	9/14/2010	2/11/2011
11	Complete Vendor System Testing	7/1/2011	7/1/2011
12	5010 Go-Live	1/2/2012	1/2/2012
13	Conduct Integrated Testing andModifications	7/1/2011	12/28/2012
14	Upgrade and Test Production Environments	12/31/2012	7/1/2013
15	Upgrade and Test Production Processes	7/2/2013	10/1/2013
16	ICD-10-CM/PCS Go-Live	10/1/2013	10/1/2013
17	Resolve System and Process Issues	10/2/2013	1/1/2014
18	Manage On-going Support	1/1/2014	1/1/2014

the documents to the project team members and stakeholders as well as make adjustments to resources and tools required for the project.

Health Information Management Implementation Process

1. Complete a Detailed Coding Assessment
2. Determine a Coding Assessment Method
3. Review Assessment Findings
4. Develop Implementation Budget, Plan, and Schedule

In most acute care facilities, the HIM department is responsible for the final inpatient claim diagnosis and procedure coding. However, within the same facility many different ancillary outpatient services are offered as well. Some examples of ancillary outpatient services are radiology tests, lab tests, oncology clinic visits, day surgery, observation, or emergency department visits. It is also necessary to assign ICD-10-CM diagnosis codes to these encounters, but the application and documentation for the diagnosis codes for these types of services may come from many different sources. Different coding assessments for these types of services, both internal and external to the HIM department, will help to define the role and effect that other facility departments will have on the HIM department implementation plan. Only with this information can the HIM department determine the best methods to decrease the risk to the facility during the ICD-10-CM transition. See appendix 2.1 for sample talking points to explain the impact of ICD-10-CM on ancillary departments.

1. Complete a Detailed Coding Assessment

The HIM department's implementation plan will require a complete detailed assessment of the daily coding operations and workflow analysis. Since inpatient procedure codes are assigned for inpatient claims only and are normally assigned by the HIM department, the ICD-10-PCS coding will not need to be addressed on the external department assessment. The assessment questionnaire will identify who within each facility department codes ICD diagnosis codes for the services provided in the facility. Figure 2.4 shows a sample HIM Coding Assessment Tool, which includes details regarding each ancillary outpatient encounter type by department, visit type, and at a minimum includes the following information:

- **Facility Department name—Examples:** Radiology, emergency department (ED), laboratory, interventional cardiology
- **Patient Encounter type—Examples:** Surgical outpatient (SOP), observation (OBV), emergency (ED), diagnostic services—This should represent the common name assigned for your facility department, such as Diagnostic Radiology (XRH)
- **Admitting, Registration, or Access Source provider (that is, where is the patient registered for service?)— Examples:** Physician office, faxed orders, electronic orders, admission office, registration office, ED, central registration, point-of-service registration (decentralized registration)
- **ICD Diagnostic Coding source (that is, who assigns the admitting and final diagnostic codes?)—Examples:** HIM, clinical department coder, charge technician, admitting or registration process, EHR, computerized coding, chargemaster, other
- **Clinical documentation source for admitting diagnosis— Examples:** Electronic order, registration diagnosis, computer assisted coding, diagnosis list, scanned paper documents, paper medical record document, EHR source document, department physician (radiologist, pathologist), other
- **Clinical documentation source document for first listed (discharge) or final diagnosis assignment—Examples:** Electronic order, registration diagnosis, computer assisted coding, scanned paper documents, paper medical record docu-

ment, EHR source document, final test impression narrative, automated code, chargemaster, other

- **Final Codes to Claim Source (that is, who is responsible for assigning the final codes to the claim?)—Examples:** HIM, clinical department, chargemaster, computer assisted, other

Each clinical or ancillary department may service many or all facility patient types and have a different coding source for each ancillary outpatient service provided. Using the assessment tool in figure 2.4, it may be necessary to fill in a box for each different encounter type more than once for the same service department. For instance, Behavioral Medicine may provide more than one type of outpatient services, such as day care and observation services. Each encounter type would be represented in the assessment grid with the clinical documentation and coding source filled in for each. Other clinical departments may not provide any ancillary outpatient services offered at all but should still be included in the assessment.

2. Determine a Coding Assessment Method

Based on the size of the facility and service departments, it may be necessary to use more than one method to obtain the information represented in figure 2.4. Determining the method for performing the coding assessment, be it written survey, telephone survey, electronic form, or any other method available, is up to the HIM project team tasked with performing the assessment.

It is important during the transition planning to assess each clinical service department to be sure the diagnosis coding source, if required, has been represented in the overall implementation plan. According to your facility, it may be best to start the clinical department assessment survey with the area with the least amount of encounters. Regardless of the assessment method of choice, once that department completes the assessment, ask for feedback on the survey tool from the people who completed the assessment. This will give you an idea

Figure 2.4. HIM ICD-10-CM coding assessment tool

Facility or Patient Service Department	Outpatient Visit Type (ex. Surgical outpatient, ED, OBV)	Patient registration (ex. Department or Central)	Admitting Diagnosis Clinical Documentation Source(s) (ex. physician order, electronic)	Final Diagnosis Clinical Documentation Source(s) (ex. test, order diagnosis, electronic)	Who assigns Final Codes to Claim Source (ex. HIM Department, electronic, chargemaster, computer assisted coding, clinical dept)
Behavioral Medicine					
Cardiac Cath Lab					
Renal Dialysis					
Emergency Department					
Heart Failure Center					
Home Health					
Hospice					
Lab					
Long-Term Care					
Nuclear Medicine					
Obstetrics					

Figure 2.4. HIM ICD-10-CM coding assessment tool (*continued*)

Oncology					
Orthopedics					
Outpatient Clinics					
Pediatrics					
Pharmacy					
Radiology–Interventional					
Radiology–Diagnostic					
Radiology–Therapeutic (other)					
Rehabilitation Services					
Respiratory					
SNF					
Surgical					
Vascular Services (non–cardiac)					
Wound Care Center					

of any additional documentation source items that may need to be included in the assessment questionnaire before deploying to other departments for completion. The important information for the HIM department to obtain from the assessment is which clinical department ancillary service's final coding they are responsible for applying the diagnostic codes to the final claim.

3. Review Assessment Findings

It is important to record the responses to the assessment for analysis. Figure 2.5, HIM Coding Source Assessment Tally Tool, can be used to tally the results from the clinical departments. The customizable file is included on the CD-ROM. However you decide to collect the responses from the coding source assessment, the information must be recorded and analyzed to determine which areas have been surveyed and if the HIM ancillary or surgical outpatient coders are responsible as the coding source. In addition, during the analysis you will gain knowledge about how you may better serve or assist the department with its ICD-10-CM educational awareness or training needs based on the complexity of the patient demographic service area for the department. You may also be able to determine whether there is substantially more risk for increasing the number of failed claims for the department with the current documentation or workflow for ICD-10-CM code assignment than currently exists with ICD-9-CM. The facility department may be better served to assign HIM to be the final ICD-10-CM diagnosis coding source for the department's claims based on the increased need for specificity in code assignment.

4. Develop Implementation Budget, Plan, and Schedule

Creation of the implementation plan is a critical task for the HIM department. The department planners should include at least one HIM coding staff member from each patient encounter type of coding responsibility that the HIM department provides for the final claim. Figure 2.6 shows a sample HIM implementation checklist. Although not comprehensive, it is an example of common HIM tasks

Figure 2.5. HIM coding source assessment tally tool

Department/Service Department	Access Source	DX Code Source	Clinical Documentation Source for Admit DX (paper order, fax order, registrant)	Clinical Documentation Source for Discharge DX (final report, ordering dx)	Final Codes to the Claim Source (dept, HIM, autodrop)
Behavioral Medicine					
Cardiac Cath Lab					
Renal Dialysis					
Emergency Department					
Heart Failure Center					
Home Health					
Hospice					
Laboratory					
Long–Term Care					
Nuclear Medicine					
Obstetrics					
Oncology					
Orthopedics					
Outpatient Clinics					

(continued on next page)

Figure 2.5.   HIM coding source assessment tally tool (*continued*)

Department/Service Department	Access Source	DX Code Source	Clinical Documentation Source for Admit DX (paper order, fax order, registrant)	Clinical Documentation Source for Discharge DX (final report, ordering dx)	Final Codes to the Claim Source (dept, HIM, autodrop)
Pediatrics					
Pharmacy					
Radiology–Diagnostic					
Radiology–Interventional					
Radiology–Therapeutic (other)					
Rehabilitation Services					
Respiratory Services					
Skilled Nursing Facility (hospital based)					
Vascular Services (noncardiac)					
Wound Care Center					

Figure 2.6. HIM coding implementation checklist

	Responsible Party	Projected Completion Date	Progress Updates	Complete Date
Develop facility Intranet site for awareness campaign				
Perform HIM coder assessment–assess coders' ICD-10 knowledge by patient encounter type they code				
Develop clinical and ancillary department ICD-10-CM and ICD-10-PCS awareness campaigns–start early				
Conduct facility coding source assessment				
Analyze coding source assessment results				
Assess department and facility coding software vendor timeline and associated costs including testing interfaces prior to Go-Live				
Assess compliance software vendor readiness timeline and budget				
Perform HIM current coding workflow analysis–reduce clerical duties where possible				
Develop coder ICD-10 education awareness plan				
Research ICD-10-CM and PCS education methodologies–cost, timeline, availability				
Develop HIM coder education budget				
Develop coder ICD-10 education schedule				

(continued on next page)

Figure 2.6. HIM coding implementation checklist (*continued*)

	Responsible Party	Projected Completion Date	Progress Updates	Complete Date
Develop coder ICD-10-PCS education schedule				
Develop ICD-10 documentation integrity team's education schedule				
Establish current HIM revenue cycle benchmarks				
Determine budget impact for potential loss of productivity during staff education				
Assess potential revenue cycle impact for temporary loss of productivity by patient type				
Determine coding productivity needs and plan accordingly for coverage during education session downtime				
Assess current contract coding vendor readiness–ICD-10 education, FTE availability				
Perform contract coding vendor analysis. How many contract coding vendors do you need to contract and train on your systems and processes prior to Go-Live?				
Establish system downtime procedures				
Review coding policies for updating and alignment with ICD-10-CM and PCS				
Perform a clinical documentation gap analysis between ICD-9-CM and ICD-10-CM/PCS for frequently assigned codes				

Figure 2.6. HIM coding implementation checklist (*continued*)

Assess or establish a postdischarge query work flow process						
Develop canned concurrent query documents for communication to physicians via e-mail, EHR, or paper records						
Develop Go–Live plan						
Design a coding staff plan for temporarily coding with both classification systems (aging encounters)						
Develop a coding support help line or Web page for other clinical departments and finance						
Develop coding support team plan for Go–Live and beyond						
Develop a "short–term" concurrent quality assessment and education plan by encounter type and department						
Develop a "long–term" post-implantation quality assessment plan and education plan by encounter type and department						
Assess productivity impact and adjust productivity accordingly (suspend temporarily or change policy permanently)						
Assess revenue cycle impact daily—interfaces, discharged, not final billed						
Assess ongoing facility coding support daily						
Report success!						

that may be necessary to perform during the transition for a successful implementation. The checklist tasks listed are in no particular order of importance and represent common items that you may encounter depending on the size and complexity of your facility and HIM department. The HIM implementation checklist may also require adding or deleting some of the tasks listed. The checklist will help the HIM department project planner clearly define and designate the HIM department's implementation plan resource needs and allow appropriate budgeting.

The implementation budget described earlier in this chapter should also be developed for the HIM area in order to plan and predict HIM expenses. (See figure 2.2.) HIM expenses may be related to additional contract coding staff requirement for temporary productivity loss, contract changes to encoder and compliance software updates, and the need for additional encoder education software enhancements, such as case analyzers or custom groupers needed.

As stated in Chapter 1, the HIM department implementation and planning schedule for beginning the implementation tasks and other requirements will be aligned closely with your facility organization-wide implementation strategy. The HIM department's plan should begin no later than early in year 2010 for the most successful transition to ICD-10-CM. In addition, if you assess the clinical departments during the years preceding implementation, it may be necessary to reassess for any updates to the information obtained from the assessments regarding changes in the clinical department code assignment and workflow processes that have occurred before implementation. Based on the size of the facility, the coding source assessment may not necessarily need to occur in 2010, but should be completed no less than 18 to 24 months before Go-Live.

With the above information obtained, the HIM Director or coding manager will now be able to more accurately predict and allocate HIM coding resources, develop a transition budget, plan for HIM department education downtime, plan HIM coding productivity, and support the clinical departments during ICD-10-CM Go-Live. One of the largest considerations to the HIM budget will be for the HIM department coder education needs. Ultimately, the organizational project committee may task the HIM department with planning the hospital's entire clinical and ancillary department coding professionals ICD-10-CM/PCS training needs and share the costs across individual department budgets.

Education of Coding Professionals

ACTION STEPS

1. Develop Education Timelines
2. Design In-House Education Sessions
3. Assess and Educate Internal Quality Improvement Personnel for Physician and Coding Staff Education
4. Determine Vendor Educational Tools

The assessment of education requirements for the current coding staff is finished, so it is important to begin focusing on timing, costs, and venues of education tailored to each individual need within the facility. The following is now known:

- Who needs education
- Intensity of educational needs
- Possible venues (for example, college courses, in-house training, consulting firms available with educational programs or seminars, and on-line education) as well as time required for these courses
- Costs associated with coder and provider education
- Software testing availability
- Whether or not new hires are required and what their educational needs are

1. Develop Education Timelines

The coding assessment coordinator or designated coding educator should develop an educational timeline 12 months before Go-Live to stagger time requirements related to the education (class attendance, study time, testing). Based on the size of the facility and number of coders, if college courses are required for some coding professionals, it may be necessary (depending on the number of coders in the facility requiring education in this venue) to begin planning 18 months in advance to allow time for obtaining transcripts and the necessary application paperwork. Consideration for time requirements of coding professionals to attend a college anatomy and physiology or medical terminology course will be class attendance (will this be scheduled at night or during the workday?), study time requirements, and testing. Reimbursement or bonus for passing the class would provide incentive to coders for time investment.

2. Design In-House Education Sessions

During regularly scheduled coder meetings, use the resources available on the Centers for Medicare & Medicaid services (CMS) ICD-10 Web site and ICD-9-CM coding workbooks, become familiar with ICD-10-CM/PCS guidelines, and apply these codes to exercises instead of ICD-9-CM codes to increase familiarity and facilitate discussion. This brings to the forefront areas of educational opportunities and stimulates discussion of potential areas for further learning. The venue also allows opportunities to update coding staff members on assessment findings and will allow them to have input into the process changes to accommodate the implementation of the updated coding system and a clear understanding of the direction the facility is headed to improve potential workload and process changes and ease backlog.

3. Assess and Educate Internal Quality Improvement Personnel for Physician and Coding Staff Education

Additionally, it is a good opportunity to determine who will fulfill the quality improvement and physician education functions. Obviously, physician and/or documentation improvement will be required in most (surgery) cases to facilitate accurate classification of the facility's patient population. Initially, development of basic presentations for provider education will be required to communicate format changes and documentation requirements related to code changes, particularly in the surgery sections. Refer to the talking points for healthcare providers in appendix 2.2.

Now is the time to consider who will be the chief or "go to" coders during the Go-Live phase of the project for quality review and education. These coders may require more exposure to educational opportunities to become the facility experts and serve as resources for the coding staff. If there are issues with rejected claims related to coding, these individuals would be an excellent resource to resolve edit conflicts encountered during the post-implementation phase of the project. It is also time to consider who will continue coding patient records requiring ICD-9-CM coding for discharges before October 1, 2013.

4. Determine Vendor Educational Tools

Discussions with vendors pertaining to educational tools as well as test products available to practice ICD-10-CM/PCS coding during this period will assist the coding staff in familiarizing themselves with the new coding system. Approximately six months before Go-Live, vendors should be asked to provide a test environment for coders to practice coding inpatient records with ICD-10-CM/PCS software. A smooth transition will be made possible if coding staff are allowed consistent periods of time during the implementation phase to use coding (and grouping, if available) software. In addition, the consistent practice will highlight educational opportunities for provider documentation, preparing for appropriate classification of the patient population accounting for patient acuity, resource consumption, and outcome data.

The focus on education of the coding and provider staff during this phase of the implementation is critical. Timely and cost efficient preparation of educational materials for coders and providers will enhance and smooth the transition to ICD-10-CM/PCS. Using vendors with software and educational packages will help minimize costs. Giving the coding staff the confidence going into the Go-Live phase with the necessary tools to accommodate an easy learning curve will minimize backlog and facilitate timely and appropriate reimbursement for the facility.

Clinical Documentation Improvement

ACTION STEPS

1. Review ICD-10-CM/PCS Changes for Impact
2. Create ICD-10-CM/PCS Awareness
3. Clinical Documentation Improvement Specialists

1. Review ICD-10-CM/PCS Changes for Impact

As the facility moves farther into the implementation plan, a closer review of the ICD-10-CM/PCS code category and detail changes and how each change may affect the business most will require review. Specialty practice clinics and facilities may experience limited impact in some areas and profound impact due to code documentation requirements in others.

2. Create ICD-10-CM/PCS Awareness

The first step in improving clinical documentation is to prepare the physician and other allied health providers for the change that is coming. Ordinarily, physicians and other allied healthcare providers are not assigning diagnostic codes, but are constructing or selecting clinical statements based on electronically selected smart text, which contain the clinical details on which the code assignment is constructed.

Begin the clinical documentation improvement plan with an education and awareness plan of the category differences directed at clinical personnel and physicians. It is best to limit your focus to the character and structural differences and to focus on the newest ICD-10-CM features available for the practice or specialty for the group. Within a facility it will be necessary, if possible, to address each clinical specialty separately.

Clinical documentation improvement efforts are most successful when facility administration and physicians are engaged in the improvement efforts. The Medical Executive Committee consists of physician leaders and administration, which directs the medical staff. A beginning approach for the project plan HIM education coordinator, director, or coding manager is to request to speak at your hospital facility's Medical Executive Committee (MEC) meeting on the topic of ICD-10-CM/PCS changes and how they will affect physicians' documentation practices at both their practices and the facilities they serve. Most hospital facilities conduct the MEC meetings on a regular basis. The MEC may then branch into clinical specialty department meetings, which will provide you a more clinical specific group to direct your education and awareness of the specific code category differences for the specialty.

The clinical groups will appreciate the focus on their specialty, and you can intersperse some other common disease category changes within the same presentation. When presenting, provide specific samples based on real cases for impact. Talking points for healthcare providers (appendix 2.2) and talking points for clinical department managers (appendix 1.3) may be used as an outline for your presentations. Also, use these tools as an intranet communication tool for your practice or facility newsletter. The more often the ICD-10-CM information is seen, the more prepared and comfortable physicians and other healthcare providers will become with the role they play in the successful transition to ICD-10-CM/PCS.

3. Clinical Documentation Improvement Specialists

As discussed in Chapter 1, clinical documentation improvement (CDI) specialists have been incorporated into many hospital facilities to help obtain more concurrently physician clinical documentation, which better substantiates the medical necessity of the inpatient.

If the facility has not already incorporated a CDI program, it may be the best time to investigate the options and benefits to incorporate a plan. Many programs are beginning to use HIM credentialed staff for their CDIS programs. Although not clinically trained in patient care, the HIM coding professional has the comprehensive background knowledge of anatomy and physiology, clinical-pathophysiology, and documentation requirements specific to diagnostic coding.

CDI employees, like the professional coding staff, will require ICD-10-CM/PCS education and awareness earlier and more continuously than those of the ancillary departments within the facility. The gaps in clinical documentation that were identified during the clinical documentation assessment, performed internally or externally by a vendor, should be the basis for the beginning work of the clinical documentation improvement process. The CDI specialists can subtly begin changing physician documentation behavior toward ICD-10-CM specificity early by asking for more specific clinical details depicted by ICD-10-CM. In order to do this, the CDI specialists must obtain the knowledge early enough to better incorporate the needed documentation details into their written or verbal interactions with the physicians and allied healthcare providers. Again, for the CDI staff, the education and awareness needs to be focused on the ICD-10-CM/PCS category detail changes, not so much on the structural differences. A successful ICD-10-CM/PCS CDI plan needs to begin early and deliver a consistent message to the providers.

A team effort between the coder and the CDI staff is essential to influence the needed clinical and procedural terminology by physician and allied healthcare providers' documentation, which will benefit the ICD-10-CM implementation project plan.

Talking Points for Ancillary Department Managers

How ICD-10 Will Affect You as an Ancillary Department Manager

OVERVIEW

The U.S. Department of Health and Human Services (HHS) has established a final rule to change the code sets to be used for reporting diagnoses and procedures on healthcare transactions. Code sets are collections of codes that are used to identify specific diagnoses and clinical procedures in claims and other transactions.

The International Classification of Diseases, ninth revision, Clinical Modification (ICD-9-CM) code set is currently used for reporting healthcare diagnoses and inpatient procedure codes in the United States.

Under the final rule, the ICD-9-CM code sets will be replaced with the International Classification of Diseases, 10th revision, Clinical Modification (ICD-10-CM) and International Classification of Diseases,

---

10th revision, Procedural Classification System (ICD–10–PCS) code sets, effective October 1, 2013.

The final rule is available at http://www.cms.hhs.gov/Transaction CodeSetsStands/02_TransactionsandCodeSetsRegulations.asp

Who Uses Codes?

- All healthcare providers use diagnostic codes for conditions, symptoms, and diseases. In the future, ICD-10-CM will be used for diagnostic codes.
- Inpatient hospitals currently use ICD-9-CM (volume 3) for procedure coding. In the future, ICD-10-PCS will be used for inpatient hospital procedure coding.
- Provider visits and ambulatory and physician procedures are coded using Current Procedural Terminology (CPT®), which is owned by the American Medical Association. In the future, CPT will continue to be used for provider visits and ambulatory and physician procedures.

ICD-10-CM Changes

- Alphanumeric—three to seven characters
- Specificity and detail significantly expanded
- ICD-10-CM has approximately 55,000 more codes than ICD-9-CM diagnosis codes
- More codes does not mean more complicated

ICD-10-CM Benefits

- Descriptive, robust categories for more precise coding; streamlined reimbursement processes; richer quality data; and treatment planning
- Maximizes value of clinical data and benefits of interoperable electronic health records (EHR) system
- Greater detail for patient, physician, and payer profiles
- Greater detail for facility and department quality reporting
- Enhanced monitoring of resource utilization

- Improving clinical, financial, and administrative performance measurement
- Data mining for patient specific populations

ICD-10-CM New Features

- Combination codes for conditions and common disease symptoms or manifestations
- Combination codes for poisonings and external causes
- Injury, external cause, and fracture extensions showing encounter of care
- Expanded codes (injury, diabetes, alcohol/substance abuse, postoperative complications)
- Added laterality
- Increased specificity
- Full code titles are used in ICD-10-CM

Examples of added laterality include:

- C50.512 Malignant neoplasm of lower-outer quadrant of left female breast
- H02.041 Spastic entropion of right upper eyelid
- M05.771 Rheumatoid arthritis with rheumatoid factor of right ankle and foot without organ or systems involvement

ICD-10-CM has combination codes for conditions and common symptoms or manifestations.

Examples include:

- I25.110 Atherosclerotic heart disease of native coronary artery with unstable angina
- K71.51 Toxic liver disease with chronic active hepatitis with ascites
- K50.012 Crohn's disease of small intestine with intestinal obstruction
- N13.731 Vesicoureteral-reflux with reflux nephropathy with hydroureter, unilateral

ICD-10-CM has combination codes for poisonings and external causes.

Examples include:

- T48.4x5A Adverse effect of expectorants, initial encounter
- T48.6x1D Poisoning by antiasthmatics, accidental (unintentional), subsequent encounter
- T46.4x6A Underdosing of angiotensin–converting–enzyme inhibitors, initial encounter
- T43.6x2S Poisoning by psychostimulants with abuse potential, intentional self-harm, sequelae

ICD-10-CM Impact

Challenges

- Revenue system and database changes
- Payer contract management
- Vendor readiness
- Payer readiness
- Potential clinical department workflow process changes
- Department staff education and awareness
- Decreased immediate code recognition among staff

Benefits

- Greater specificity and detail for:
  —Medical necessity
  —Diagnostic research
  —Physician profiles
  —Quality management reporting
  —Pay for performance reporting
  —Department utilization management
  —Contract management
  —Public reporting

Conversion

- Plan for ICD-10-CM training for all impacted department staff
- Work with vendors to obtain upgraded software to accommodate expanded field lengths and code changes
- Check CMS Medicare Learning Network for changes in coverage policies
- Retain access to historical coded data
- System field lengths must be expanded to accommodate expanded data element length
- Understand the impact to payment systems and assess impact of those changes
- Determination of impacts on facility revenue cycle
- Review of storage and reporting practices for longitudinal data
- Staff awareness plan

Processes

- Department staff training assessment
- Patient registration for the department processes
- Advanced beneficiary notice department processes
- Reporting needs for departments utilizing coded data
- National and local coverage determinations edits
- System logic and edits (for example, medical necessity)
- Provider profiling
- Quality measurement and quality initiatives reporting
- Claims editing
- Claims data analysis
- Utilization management
- Disease management
- Aggregate data reporting

Frequently Asked Questions

Is ICD-10-CM mainly intended for hospital inpatient coding?

No, ICD-10-CM will replace ICD-9-CM diagnosis codes and will be used for reporting all diagnoses regardless of setting.

Will the increased number of ICD-10-CM diagnoses codes lead to an increase in the number of claims processed?

No, claims will continue to be paid based on CPT and HCPCS codes. They will capture diagnoses on their bills using ICD-10-CM. The increased specificity in the ICD-10-CM code may lead to a reduction in bills that are returned for additional information. Precise diagnosis codes provide more information about the service. They do not lead to additional claims or payment.

What can organizations do now to prepare for implementation of ICD-10-CM?

- Identify stakeholders
- Assess impact to every department
- Formulate strategies and identify goals
- Develop education and training plans for employees at all levels
- Develop information systems and technology systems change implementation plan

ICD-10 Resources

- AHIMA's ICD-10 Web site
  http://www.ahima.org/icd10/
- General ICD-10-CM Information
  http://www.cms.hhs.gov/ICD10/

- Fact Sheet: HHS MODIFIES HIPAA CODE SETS (ICD-10) AND ELECTRONIC TRANSACTIONS STANDARDS
  http://www.cms.hhs.gov/apps/media/fact_sheets.asp
- To read the HHS press release issued on ICD-10:
  http://www.hhs.gov/news/press/2008pres/2008.html
- January 2009 Release of ICD-10-CM, which includes Preface, Index, Tabular List, Table of Drugs and Chemicals and General Equivalence Mapping Files
  http://www.cdc.gov/nchs/about/otheract/icd9/abticd10.htm

Talking Points for Healthcare Providers

How ICD-10 Will Affect You as a Healthcare Provider

OVERVIEW

The U.S. Department of Health and Human Services (HHS) has established a final rule to change the code sets to be used for reporting diagnoses and procedures on healthcare transactions. Code sets are collections of codes that are used to identify specific diagnoses and clinical procedures in claims and other transactions.

The International Classification of Diseases, ninth revision, Clinical Modification (ICD-9-CM) code set is currently used for reporting healthcare diagnoses and inpatient procedure codes in the United States.

Under the final rule, the ICD-9-CM code sets will be replaced with the International Classification of Diseases, 10th revision, Clinical Modification (ICD-10-CM) and International Classification of Diseases, 10th revision, Procedural Classification System (ICD-10-PCS) code sets, effective October 1, 2013.

Disclaimer

This material was prepared as a service to the public and is not intended to grant rights or impose obligations. This publication may contain references or links to statutes, regulations, or other policy materials. The information provided is intended only to be a general summary. It is not intended to take the place of either the written law or regulations. We encourage readers to review the specific statutes, regulations, and other interpretive materials for a full and accurate statement of their contents.

The final rule is available at http://www.cms.hhs.gov/Transaction
CodeSetsStands/02_TransactionsandCodeSetsRegulations.asp

Who Uses Codes?

- All healthcare providers use diagnostic codes for conditions, symptoms, and diseases. In the future, ICD-10-CM will be used for diagnostic codes.
- Inpatient hospitals currently use ICD-9-CM (volume 3) for procedure coding. In the future, ICD-10-PCS will be used for inpatient hospital procedure coding.
- Provider visits and ambulatory and physician procedures are coded using Current Procedural Terminology (CPT®), which is owned by the American Medical Association. In the future, CPT will continue to be used for provider visits and ambulatory and physician procedures.

ICD-10-CM Changes

- Alphanumeric
- Specificity and detail significantly expanded

ICD-10-PCS Changes

- Seven character alphanumeric
- Each character has a consistent meaning throughout the code set
- Root operation specifies the objective of procedure

ICD-10-CM Benefits

- Descriptive, robust categories for more precise coding; streamlined reimbursement processes; richer quality data; and treatment planning
- Maximizes value of clinical data and benefits of interoperable electronic health records system
- Greater detail for patient and physician profiles
- Greater detail for quality reporting
- Enhanced monitoring of resource utilization

- Improving clinical, financial, and administrative performance measurement
- Expanded capability to prevent and detect healthcare fraud and abuse
- Tracking public health risks

ICD-10-CM New Features

- Combination codes for conditions and common disease symptoms or manifestations
- Combination codes for poisonings and external causes
- Injury, external cause, and fracture extensions showing episode of care
- Expanded codes (injury, diabetes, alcohol/substance abuse, postoperative complications)
- Added laterality
- Increased specificity
- Full code titles are used in ICD-10-CM

Examples of added laterality in ICD-10:

- C50.512 Malignant neoplasm of lower-outer quadrant of left female breast
- H02.041 Spastic entropion of right upper eyelid
- M05.771 Rheumatoid arthritis with rheumatoid factor of right ankle and foot without organ or systems involvement

ICD-10-CM has combination codes for conditions and common symptoms or manifestations.

Examples include:

- I25.110 Atherosclerotic heart disease of native coronary artery with unstable angina
- K71.51 Toxic liver disease with chronic active hepatitis with ascites
- K50.012 Crohn's disease of small intestine with intestinal obstruction
- N13.731 Vesicoureteral-reflux with reflux nephropathy with hydroureter, unilateral

ICD-10-CM has combination codes for poisonings and external causes.

Examples include:

- T48.4x5A Adverse effect of expectorants, initial encounter
- T48.6x1D Poisoning by antiasthmatics, accidental (unintentional), subsequent encounter
- T46.4x6A Underdosing of angiotensin-converting-enzyme inhibitors, initial encounter
- T43.6x2S Poisoning by psychostimulants with abuse potential, intentional self-harm, sequelae

ICD-10-CM Impact

Challenges

- Clinical documentation will need greater specificity

Benefits

- Codes are specific to type of complication and in some cases linked to specific procedures
- Ability to use specific coded data for Present on Admission (POA) and Potentially Preventable Events (PPE) determinations in future payment to healthcare providers
- Greater specificity for pay-for-performance programs and medical necessity

Impact of Conversion to ICD-10-CM

- Plan for ICD-10-CM training for all impacted staff
- Work with vendors to obtain upgraded software to accommodate expanded field lengths and code changes
- Check CMS Medicare Learning Network for changes in coverage policies
- Update superbills/encounter forms and databases
- Retain access to historical coded data

Conversion

- System field lengths must be expanded to accommodate expanded data element length
- Understand the impact to payment systems and assess impact of those changes
- Determination of impacts on revenue cycle
- Review of storage and reporting practices for longitudinal data
- Impact and training needs assessments for physicians, clinicians, nursing, and ancillary department education
- Staff awareness plan
- Clinical documentation training
- Impact assessment on staff and physician technology (hand-helds, etc.)

Processes

- MS-DRG conversion
- Conversion of other payment methodologies dependent on diagnosis/procedure codes
- National and local coverage determinations
- System logic and edits (for example, medical necessity)
- Provider profiling
- Quality measurement and quality initiatives
- Claims editing
- Claims data analysis
- Utilization management
- Disease management
- Aggregate data reporting

Frequently Asked Questions

Is ICD-10-CM mainly intended for hospital inpatient coding?

No, ICD-10-CM will replace ICD-9-CM diagnosis codes and will be used for reporting all diagnoses regardless of setting.

Will the increased number of ICD-10-CM diagnoses codes lead to an increase in the number of physician bills?

No, physicians will continue to be paid based on CPT and HCPCS codes. They will capture diagnoses on their bills using ICD-10-CM. The increased specificity in the ICD-10-CM code may lead to a reduction in bills that are returned for additional information. For instance, when patients sought evaluation and care because of possible exposure to anthrax, there was no ICD-9-CM code to clearly indicate the reason for the encounter. It was only after the creation of new and specific anthrax codes that we were able to track encounters and outcomes using a precise diagnosis code. Precise diagnosis codes provide more information about the service. They do not lead to additional bills or payment.

What can organizations do now to prepare for implementation of ICD-10?

- Identify stakeholders
- Assess impact
- Formulate strategies and identify goals
- Develop education/training plans for employees at all levels
- Develop information systems/technology systems change implementation plan

ICD-10 Resources

- AHIMA's ICD-10 Web site
  http://www.ahima.org/icd10/
- General ICD-10-CM Information
  http://www.cms.hhs.gov/ICD10/
- Fact Sheet: HHS MODIFIES HIPAA CODE SETS (ICD-10) AND ELECTRONIC TRANSACTIONS STANDARDS
  http://www.cms.hhs.gov/apps/media/fact_sheets.asp

- To read the HHS press release issued on ICD-10:
  http://www.hhs.gov/news/press/2008pres/2008.html
- January 2009 Release of ICD-10-CM, which includes Preface,
  Index, Tabular List, Table of Drugs and Chemicals, and General
  Equivalence Mapping Files
  http://www.cdc.gov/nchs/about/otheract/icd9/abticd10.htm

Go-Live Preparation

Once the assessment and gap analysis activities have been completed, the next step is to begin preparations for Go-Live activities, including system modifications, procedural changes, and beginning staff education events. Go-Live activities start at the tail end of testing, education, and new system or process set-up in preparation for the Go-Live date. For the ICD-10-CM/PCS regulation, Go-Live is scheduled for October 1, 2013, meaning patients discharged on October 1, 2013 will have their records coded using ICD-10-CM/PCS and claims processed with the same codes. Depending on how current your facility is with coding discharged records, you may be submitting ICD-10-CM/PCS records on October 2nd; however, each organization should pick the date all new services and processes are put in place. Because new services and processes are not directly a part of the regulation, organizations may decide to begin their production activities either before or after the ICD-10-CM/PCS implementation date. Therefore, actual Go-Live dates events may range from a day to several months depending on the amount of changes being made at your facility. Go-Live events are critical to the success of a project and great care must be taken for proper planning and execution. This chapter describes the preparation steps for the Go-Live activities in order to meet regulation deadlines in addition to the production deadline you have established to be included in the project.

Organization-wide Implementation Strategy

ACTION STEPS

1. Determine Go-Live Activities
2. Compile Go-Live Documents
3. Distribute the Comprehensive Go-Live Plan

The term "Go-Live" can have multiple meanings ranging from the first date a specific aspect of an application is used to the first date and time an entire system or process is being used. This book refers to Go-Live as the date for complying with the federal regulations deadline for 5010 and ICD-10-CM/PCS implementation, focusing on the latter. The compliance dates stated in the final rules are as follows:

- 5010 transaction standards:
  —X12 Version 5010 (some healthcare transactions) and Version D.0 (pharmacy transactions—January 1, 2012
  —Version 3.0 (Medicaid pharmacy subrogation transaction)—January 1, 2012
  —Version 3.0—small health plans—January 1, 2013
- ICD-10-CM and ICD-10-PCS—October 1, 2013

Although it may appear that these dates are in the fairly distant future, the time allotted by CMS to comply with the regulations is geared toward giving healthcare facilities plenty of time to complete testing and implementation activities if they are started early in 2009. The most important of all preparation activities is to develop a Go-Live plan. Adequate time taken in the planning phase can mitigate negative outcomes, commonly referred to as the five Ps:

Prior
Planning
Prevents
Poor
Performance

1. Determine Go-Live Activities

The implementation and utilization of ICD-10-CM/PCS code sets is quite extensive given the multilevel coordination required among the organization as a whole, each department, and vendors. The Go-Live event is the day on which ICD-9-CM and ICD-10-CM/PCS codes are entered and submitted through the appropriate billing systems and to payers simultaneously. For this event to be successful, all systems modifications, testing activities, and coordination must be successfully completed on the same day. This Go-Live event will be like no other your organization has experienced, and when executed extremely well will still result in issues requiring examination and resolution. The project timeline must be realistic and accommodate issues that will arise during and throughout the Go-Live event(s). A well thought-out Go-Live plan anticipates issues and accommodates for them with appropriate response plans and resources. Appendix C includes a sample Go-Live plan to be modified by your organization in preparation for the compliance deadlines. A customizable file is included on the CD-ROM.

2. Compile Go-Live Documents

The Go-Live plan development should be a coordinated event with all team members (senior management, information systems [IS], ancillary departments, and health information management [HIM] department) and done once the final project schedule is finalized. Preparation for the Go-Live can occur only after the gap analysis and assessment activities have been completed and steps to complete the project activities are known, even if some of the outcomes remain unknown. Go-Live preparation activities start with system and process updates, testing, and validation activities to prepare software, training, and communication for end-users and infrastructure changes to prepare the workspaces. The Go-Live plan is a document that compiles the multiple plans developed for each change, including people, processes, and technology, into a single comprehensive document for the project team to reference. A comprehensive Go-Live plan is extensive; however, organizations that have this information find it very beneficial and worth the time to develop its content. A Go-Live plan will include the following sections:

■ Activity Participant List

   Identify all participants in the Go-Live activities. This will include members of the project team, vendor team, steering committee, senior management, and other resources required to complete all tasks and communication related to the Go-Live activities.

- Roles and Responsibilities

  Each participant identified above needs to be defined under the roles and responsibilities so that it is clear to all participants who is responsible for completing the activities. Every participant, no matter how minor his or her role, must be listed to ensure the appropriate resources are included in the communications.

- Tools and Resources Needed

  Go-Live activities may require additional workstations, Internet or intranet connections, team members, and so forth for the project team to successfully complete the Go-Live activities. This is a documented list of all tools and resources needed for the activities. When compiling the list, think about what tools or resources are required for success. Without these tools, the activity will either fail or have consequences, thus negatively impacting Go-Live. An example includes the availability of the Internet in a new area; without it, the computer systems cannot connect to the appropriate applications, resulting in claims not being processed. The information in this section may need to include justification for the executive team to approve. In this case, adjust the template to accommodate additional comments or information to support the request. Supporting documents can also be added to the end of the document or included as supplementary information.

- Key Milestones

  Project milestones are completed throughout the project; the key milestones on this list are those that are required for Go-Live to be successful. These milestones may include software upgrades, hardware upgrades, testing activities, resource training, and communication activities. All milestones listed here are important to the success of Go-Live (submitting ICD-10-CM/PCS codes for reimbursement successfully).

■ Activity Timeline

Project tasks roll up on the project schedule to project milestones, and project activities roll up to project tasks; however, project activities are not always detailed on a project schedule. The activity timeline documents all activities and due dates that are required to meet project tasks and project milestones outlined in the project schedule. An example of a project activity rolling up into the project tasks and finally into the project milestone is as follows:

Project Milestone: Coding Software Product Upgrade

Project Tasks:
1. Complete Training
2. Complete Testing
3. Complete Validation
4. Complete Sign-off on Product

Project Activities:
1. Complete Training:
    a. Reserve Training Environment
    b. Schedule Training Resources
    c. Configure Training Workstations and Environment
    d. Complete Training Activities
    e. Attendees Complete Training Validation Documents
    f. Complete Testing:
    g. Schedule Testing Activities with Resources (location, people)
2. Configure Test Server
    a. Configure Test Applications
    b. Configure Test Interfaces
3. Validate Test User Settings
    a. Validate Test Resources Schedules
4. Complete Testing Phase I Scenario 1
    a. Inpatient Records MRN 0034566, 0098445, 904587
5. Complete Validation Phase I Scenario 1
    a. Inpatient Records MRN 0034566, 0098445, 904587

As shown above, project activities are much more detailed than project tasks; however, they should not be made so detailed that they become unrealistic. It is helpful to think about list-ing activities that are important versus those that are obvious. The activities listed need to be detailed enough for each per-son completing the tasks to fully understand what needs to be completed. If the resources completing the tasks are not very experienced, more details are necessary. Each project team will need to provide the details of the project activities, as they will be completing the activities as well as assigning the resources and will know how detailed the list needs to be made.

■ Communication Plan

The Go-Live events, including the day(s) of Go-Live are typi-cally very busy, and communication can easily be overlooked. Documenting a communication plan enables the project team to strategize how best to communicate with all levels of the project members, including project leads, project manager, steering committee members, executive sponsor, and project stakeholders, such as physicians. Communication detail levels can vary depending on the audience receiving the commu-nication messages and the form of communication, such as e-mail, phone, or Internet. The project leadership team should determine the best means of communication throughout the project, including Go-Live activities, as well as the appropriate resources to deliver the communication. The communication plan lays out all the messages that are expected throughout Go-Live activities, the responsible resources who will send the messages, message formats, and who will receive them.

■ Activity Back-out Plan

The Go-Live activities will have results, including some nega-tive that require adjustment or some irreversible that require a Plan B, or a back-out plan. While we do not expect to experience catastrophic events that require you to use Plan B, it is best to have an action plan so you know what to do in case of the occurrence. Software systems are the changes with the highest risk for requiring a back-out plan; however, any change being made to people, processes, or technologies should be evaluated for risk, and a back-out plan should be developed for all those that are required to operate business functions on a daily basis. Back-out plans include activities that will take place to determine the extent of the problem, alternate systems, processes, resources that can be implemented to complete business functions, and an estimate of time required to determine next steps in resolving the issue. The back-out plan needs to simply identify the action steps and resources needed to resolve the immediate issue, not solve the entire problem. In the case of a catastrophic software issue, most likely a developer, who is not a part of the project team, will need to resolve the issue. Therefore, the back-out plan would determine what alternate systems or versions can be used in the interim while the appropriate resources are resolving the issue identified.

■ Activity Support Schedule

Go-Live activities may span extended hours, days, and weeks; therefore, it is best to have scheduled resources identified ahead of time to ensure that appropriate staffing is available to support the Go-Live activities. If software system conversions are required and estimated to last into the overnight hours, relief resources are necessary to assist with supporting the conversion to help eliminate resource mistakes that may occur due to fatigue. The activity support schedule is designed to identify and schedule resources that can support the resources completing Go-Live activities.

■ Problem Reporting Guide

Issues will be identified throughout Go-Live, and in order to keep the issues cataloged and managed so that resolution is ensured and follow-up is completed, a problem reporting guide is necessary. This guide provides instructions to team members completing testing and validation activities as to how to appropriately collect process or system error information and report the error so it can be corrected by the appropriate resources in a timely manner. The closer your organization is to Go-Live dates, the more important it will be to expedite issue resolution. The problem reporting guide can be made as specific as necessary for every area undergoing change, including software and processes.

3. Distribute the Comprehensive Go-Live Plan

The Go-Live activity plan compiled by the core project team should be distributed among the project team members, project sponsors, vendors, and stakeholders. The plan is a living document and should be adjusted and redistributed as activities are completed. Timelines are likely to shift as activities are completed and as adjustments are required and completed. Updated plans should be distributed along with other project reporting documents.

Information Systems Go-Live Preparation Activities

ACTION STEPS

1. Develop the Go-Live Plan
2. Prepare Testing Environments
    2.1 Software Test Environments
    2.2 Hardware Test Environments
3. Complete Testing Activities
    3.1 Develop Test Scenarios
    3.2 Assign Testing Resources
4. Schedule Go-Live Activities
5. Complete Go-Live Events and Activities

Activities included in Go-Live preparation are completed with the intent of transitioning processes or systems starting on a single day (Go-Live), moving forward with a cut and dry transition event. On the Go-Live day, systems will simultaneously support and transmit ICD-9-CM and ICD-10-CM/PCS code sets while new processes or services will begin. The duration for supporting both code set formats is specific to each organization and will depend on how up-to-date the facility is with coding discharged records, the turnaround time for settling submitted claim information, as well as how long organizations need to keep data to accommodate audits, release of information, and research projects. Until all claims submitted for patients discharged before October 1, 2013, have been completed, audited, paid, and all uses for data collected in the ICD-9-CM format, both versions must remain operable and referable. Claims for patients discharged starting at midnight on October 1, 2013, will be required to be formatted with ICD-10-CM/PCS codes. Claim transmissions on October 2nd may include ICD-9-CM and ICD-10-CM/PCS codes depending on the date of discharge for each patient. Additionally, if payers are unable to comply with the regulation, organizations will need to be prepared to accommodate the issue until a resolution has been reached. It will be important for the IS team to work closely with the finance and billing departments, as well as the HIM team, to ensure adequate testing of all systems and applications to fully comply with the transaction regulations.

1. Develop the Go-Live Plan

The IS Go-Live plan will include a detailed testing activity plan. Outline the events and expected results, and the specific resources required to complete each testing phase performed throughout the preparation activities. The multiple departments and vendors involved in the coordination and completion of testing and preparation activities must be scheduled and fully documented. Communication of all testing events and results to all team members and vendors will ensure that the Go-Live preparation activities are as seamless as possible. Due to the complexity of this implementation, actions to resolve issues should be anticipated, and a thorough plan will include plenty of time for mitigation throughout the entire schedule. The template in Appendix C and included in the CD-ROM details the final preparation activities;

however, the work of Go-Live should begin as soon as the assessment activities end. Knowledge gained during the assessment and gap
analysis processes will provide the project team with Go-Live risks
and identify potential issues.

2. Prepare Testing Environments

The first step in preparing for testing activities includes setting up
the testing environments. A testing environment includes hardware,
software, training documentation, processes and system diagrams, and
team members to complete the testing activities.

2.1. Software Test Environments

Software environments for test purposes must be separate from the
production environment and dedicated to the testing activities. Organizations have several options for building a dedicated test system and
all have pros and cons that will need to be carefully addressed by the
project team. These options are outlined below:

   a. **Copy Production Data into the Test Systems**—This type
      of a testing system is most realistic when it comes to valid data
      being used for testing purposes; however, it includes produc-
      tion demographic information and may need to be carefully
      thought out as all system information for patients must match.
      If you choose to copy production data into a test environment,
      you will need to select the dates of services you are copying
      and include all systems impacted by the change. If data are
      older than those stored in specific systems, such as interfaces,
      you may need to copy data for a given period of time, then
      turn on production interfaces to continue to populate produc-
      tion data. The risk with relying on interfaces to populate pro-
      duction data is that some data required for testing may not be
      transmitted by interfaces and may require manual updates to
      complete testing activities. The benefit of using this scenario is
      in volume testing because typical test environments with only
      test data do not produce the same volume as the production

environment; therefore, some issues that arise as a result in volumes of data being transmitted will not be discovered during testing and can cause issues at Go-Live.

b. **Utilize Test Data in the Test Systems**—Test data can be preferred as they can be initiated in systems farthest upstream and move data all the way though applications from end to end with very specific criteria. Production data do not always include all scenarios as some are rare and are not present in the current environment. Test data can also be helpful to limit the volume of data that resources need to review to complete testing activities.

Either option is appropriate depending on the procedures at your organization. The most important information to include in testing is that all patient types, service types, payers, and situations identified in the testing plan have been set up in a test environment to be tested. Do not take shortcuts in testing; it will cost you in the production environment with this type of an implementation. Take the time needed to set up the most appropriate system and complete testing activities.

2.2. Hardware Test Environments

Test systems may require separate hardware depending on the set-up of the applications. Organizations may not even have a test environment for all applications required to be tested and will first need to determine if the environment exists or if it needs to be created. The IS team will need to work with the software vendors to determine the best test environment for the project based on the requirements of the organization and elements required for testing and validation activities. Hardware replacement projects may be included in this transition and should be incorporated into the testing plan because new hardware may require applications to be installed and validated, requiring downtime for end-users. If end-users are in a testing environment and away from their desk, the IS team can take advantage of that workstation downtime and install new technology.

3. Complete Testing Activities

The final regulations include a phased approach to testing, beginning with internal applications and functionality before integrating activities with external vendors. A planned and scheduled approach that anticipates risk areas is most productive. Construct a testing plan that builds upon itself as specific testing milestones are completed. Upon the completion of the 5010 implementation in January 2011, organizations should begin testing applications with the transmission of both ICD-9-CM and ICD-10-CM/PCS codes. This action will help identify issues as early as possible in the testing phase and allow time for mitigation. Some vendors will not be as responsive as others in participating in testing and modification activities. This implementation is the largest project any vendor has completed, and work with the external vendors should begin as early as possible to get on their schedule and have resources assigned. Some vendors who initially believe their software will be compliant with the ICD-10-CM/PCS regulations will find they are unfortunately unable to meet the compliance requirements, and they will need to be replaced. Finding out information such as this early will give your organization time to replace the vendor and complete implementation and testing activities.

3.1 Develop Test Scenarios

Scenarios used to verify all areas of technology required for testing are included in the plan. The project team should work together to develop test scenarios that are comprehensive and cover all application functionality, interfaces, databases, reports, and processes included in the transition. Test scenarios documented in the testing schedule must include resources assigned to ensure the steps in the test are validated and approved. Testing may be completed in phases as more and more systems are linked together for the complete claims transmission process. Scenario writing should accommodate the specific testing phases and elements the project team, as well as vendor team, deem necessary to test during each phase.

The application testing results spreadsheet on the CD-ROM includes a sample testing plan to be modified for each software application incorporated into the testing and Go-Live preparation activities. A snapshot of this tool is included in figure 3.1.

3.2 Assign Testing Resources

Testing scenarios should be assigned to project team members and include end-users of specific applications whenever possible. The advantage of using end-users to complete testing activities is that it reinforces their knowledge of the application as well as the expected functionality. People with experience using an application are much more likely to catch an irregularity as opposed to someone who has just recently learned the application or process. Including coders in testing activities is extremely important because it will give them opportunities to code using ICD-10-CM/PCS code sets prior to the production date. The more familiar end-users are with new technology and processes, the more successful they will be using it.

Testing resources should be scheduled to complete the testing scenarios and provide the results of each scenario to the appropriate project resources. Resources should be able to cover multiple areas in the testing scenarios and have assigned back-ups if they are unable to complete testing activities themselves. If an issue is identified during testing, the appropriate team members should deal with the issue according to the process outlined in the Problem Reporting Guide. The project manager, in coordination with the IS and HIM team leads, should work to identify and resolve issues as timely as possible to keep the Go-Live on schedule. Software system functionality is essential and therefore on the project critical path as it can directly stall the project if not functioning as expected. Applications not compliant with the regulations by the dates defined within the project schedule could result in rejected claims and have financial implications. Project team members should take action to begin preparation activities for testing as soon as possible to identify and resolve issues sooner rather than later. Testing activities are a coordinated event and

Figure 3.1. ICD-10-CM/PCS application testing plan and results

Purpose: The purpose of the ICD-10-CM and ICD-10-PCS application testing plan and results worksheets is to identify the functionality within each application impacted by the transition, as well as detail the expected results and outcomes of the application.

Project Information

Project Manager

Budget Manager

Project Sponsor

Project Start Date mm/dd/yyyy

Last Modified Date mm/dd/yyyy

Testing Plan

Testing activities and assigned resources are detailed in the Go-Live plan. Testing activity worksheets should be developed for each application involved in Go-Live preparation activities.

Testing Results

All results produced from testing activities should be communicated to the resources identified and outlined in the Go-Live plan.

Figure 3.1. ICD-10-CM/PCS application testing plan and results *(continued)*

Applications Included in Testing Activities

Application	Software System	Vendor
Application Name	*System Name*	*Vendor Name*
Application Name	*System Name*	*Vendor Name*
Application Name	*System Name*	*Vendor Name*

ICD-10-CM and ICD-10-PCS Testing Results

Software System Name:							
Vendor Name:							

Module	Function	Expected Results	Results	Pass	Fail	Comments	Actions	Testing Resource	Date
1									
2									
3									

should be as comprehensive as possible to take advantage of the time dedicated by the internal and external testing resources.

4. Schedule Go-Live Activities

The Go-Live activities may require systems to be converted from the test environment to the production environment and therefore applications may need to be taken down and unavailable for an extended period of time. Plan for system downtime, which can directly and widely impact productivity and adversely affect patient care. It is vital to maintain constant operability of systems critical to delivering patient care. Planning for Go-Live includes scheduling downtime with end-users, clinicians, staff, and vendors. The plan should include workarounds for accessing important information during downtime, and contingencies for systems that do not come back up as expected. In addition to preparation for system downtime, resource and process impacts need to be evaluated as well. Significant downtime may require resource schedules to be adjusted to ether increase or decrease the number of staff available to participate in the Go-Live events. Communication to end-users of any downtime or alterations to their work schedules throughout the project is important, especially during the Go-Live event when stress may escalate. If you are scheduled to complete multiple activities with extended resource commitments, consider bringing in additional staff to help offset the workload and avoid staff burnout. The Go-Live schedule for activities post-testing specific to transitioning systems from test to production environment to accommodate the ICD-10-CM/PCS codes, including resource allocation, should be completed and approved by the project team and steering committee at least 60 days prior to the initial Go-Live milestone. This will allow for sufficient time to plan and prepare for the event.

5. Complete Go-Live Events and Activities

Go-Live events can result in stressful situations and crises if the level of effort applied to planning for the event activities is insufficient. The best planned Go-Live will still include unforeseen issues that must be resolved quickly. Be sure to allocate and schedule resources and facilities for handling issues throughout Go-Live activities. These activities start with the integrated testing and conclude after the production environments are actively transmitting ICD-10-CM/PCS codes successfully. The validation and issue resolution process usually takes a minimum of 30 days post Go-Live. The goal of this toolkit is to help you prepare for the Go-Live events and issues that will occur throughout Go-Live. It is very important to plan and be prepared for worst-case scenarios during months in which the work is completed. When situations that require a resolution arise at your facility, monitor the allocated staffing levels and re-assess frequently to determine if additional resources are needed. At Go-Live, team members can expect to have worked long hours, and simple mistakes due to fatigue can cost organizations much more time and money than the cost to add resources to provide assistance. Schedule daily or periodic debriefings with the project team during the Go-Live activities to ensure that tasks are completed and communicated to the team. Debriefings also allow a forum for and appropriate brainstorming to resolve surprises. Communication is the key to a successful Go-Live, and keeping a healthy team dynamic will help everyone stay focused on the end goal.

Health Information Management Go-Live Preparation Activities

ACTION STEPS

1. Develop an External Coding Support Team
2. Develop an HIM Department Coding Support Team
3. Develop a Coding Work Distribution Plan
4. Develop a Communication Plan

The HIM implementation assessment provides a great deal of information for Go-Live planning. All parties must be prepared and know their roles and expectations. The sample Go-Live checklist in figure 3.2 is a starting point to assign tasks for the Go-Live plan in appendix C.

A customizable file is included on the CD-ROM. Healthcare services provided on or after October 1, 2013, require ICD-10-CM/PCS code assignment. It is imperative to have a plan for daily interaction and support among the HIM department, coders, and ancillary departments.

1. Develop an External Coding Support Team

The HIM department Go-Live plan begins with completing the comprehensive training for the coders and other department staff members who are responsible for assigning or interpreting ICD-10-CM/PCS codes. Consider establishing a temporary help desk. This can reduce failed claims because of edits or unnecessary holding of claims due to unclear documentation specificity. At a minimum, a temporary supporting communication tool linked to one or more HIM coding experts should be communicated and established to support the follow-up ancillary departments:

- Clinical departments (decentralized registration)
- Clinical documentation improvement (CDI) department staff
- Hospital-based outpatient clinic physician practice coders
- Patient access services (centralized registration)
- Patient financial services

The help desk may be as sophisticated as a link on the facility's intranet site with e-mail service or a live chat function on your hospital's external Web site, or as simple as a contact name and telephone number. However you choose to provide the resource, the most important part is to notify the external departments of the temporary service. The communication must define the service's purpose, provide an expected response time to the user, and be communicated to the resources that are most likely to best use the service before and after Go-Live. The temporary help desk should remain intact until an acceptable benchmark established by the Go-Live team is reached based on the incoming volume of requests.

Figure 3.2. HIM Go-Live checklist

Process	Date	Responsible Person	Completed
HIM dept. coding staff and super users trained		HIM	
Physicians and allied health providers educated for documentation		HIM	
Training of hospital and ancillary department staff completed		HIM	
Contract coding vendor readiness established		HIM	
Software for remote coders installed and tested		Hospital/IS	
Encoder to finance systems interfacing with ICD-10 codes completed		Hospital/IS	
Remote coder access to standalone encoder established		HIM/IS Support	
Coding work distribution plan established and communicated		HIM	
Coding system down-time procedures established		HIM	
Post-discharge query process established		HIM	
Report on coder productivity completed		HIM	
Report on average volume of physician query deficiency counts completed		HIM	
Report on current discharge not final billed counts completed – all patient types		HIM	
Report on failed claims completed		HIM	
Process for HIM coder to coder questions established		HIM	

(continued on next page)

Figure 3.2.   HIM Go-Live checklist *(continued)*

Process	Date	Responsible Person	Completed
Ancillary dept. coding support help desk established (Web, phone, other)		HIM	
Clinical documentation support staff coding resource established		HIM	
Physician coding support help desk established (Web, phone, other)		HIM	
Resources to coding help desk assigned (Web, phone, other)		HIM	
Communication of coding help desk to users completed		HIM	
Data quality reviewer list created		HIM	
Process for data quality reviewers established		HIM	
Test to review queue in compliance software assigned		HIM	
Charts in coding compliance and quality review queues reviewed		HIM	
HIM dept. Go-Live communication plan established		HIM	
Go-Live processing begins		HIM	

2. Develop an HIM Department Coding Support Team

To reduce the impact on the revenue cycle, the HIM department coding staff will need the most responsive ICD-10-CM/PCS support. If possible, an ICD-10-CM/PCS data quality coordinator should be assigned to concurrently assist and respond to coders' questions regarding code assignment or to assist in communicating the appropriate physician query with detail for greater specificity. Establish a mechanism for the data quality and the help desk coordinators to collect questions to create a frequently asked questions (FAQ) area that can remain on your Web site post-implementation. FAQs can help identify continuous process improvement projects to tackle after Go-Live.

3. Develop a Coding Work Distribution Plan

Another item to include in the HIM department Go-Live plan is the distribution of duties. The HIM director or coding manager will decide if one or more coders should begin immediately coding the records that need ICD-10-CM/PCS codes assigned, versus coders using ICD-9-CM and having to work between the two coding systems. Limiting the ICD-10-CM/PCS work distribution to fewer coders may ameliorate overload. Splitting the responsibilities between the two coding systems may make for a smoother transition to complete dissemination of work to the rest of the coding staff.

As part of ramping up for the Go-Live plan, it is important to know the existing status and volume of outstanding work—such as the amount of physician queries and discharges not final billed—in order to predict productivity changes that ICD-10-CM/PCS may have to coding operations and the revenue cycle.

4. Develop a Communication Plan

The Go-Live plan should also include communication procedures. For example, the HIM project lead and a patient financial services representative should have a regularly scheduled daily or weekly meeting to discuss and fix any system interface or other issues that may have an immediate impact on the revenue cycle. It is important to involve the IS department in your communication plan. An example of items to discuss during the regular meetings includes the following:

- Updates on any outstanding documentation issues
- Status of the advanced beneficiary notice processes
- Registration issues
- Volume of held claims due to claim edits

It is extremely critical for the HIM department during Go-Live to collaborate with clinical departments and patient financial services. It is also important to engage the hospital administration in supporting physicians, clinical department managers, and ancillary patient registration staff for any needs you may encounter during Go-Live.

Education of Coding Professionals

ACTION STEPS

1. Monitor Internal Editing and Quality Issues
2. Conduct Weekly Status Meetings
3. Provide Ongoing Feedback to Coding and Physician Staff

We have now reached the Go-Live phase of the project. All departments are working toward the same objective with the new classification system. It is likely that questions may arise that were not thought about during the initial planning or that processes require further refinement. At this point, everyone involved in the project should communicate effectively to resolve and mitigate any unanticipated issues. The assessment and implementation plan has helped facilitate decisions such as the following:

- Who will continue with the ICD-9-CM coding until all records are coded?
- Who will perform quality checks and ongoing assistance for coding staff performing ICD-10-CM/ICD-10-PCS coding?
- Who will continue educating physician/provider staff?
- Who will follow up with physician/provider staff regarding further documentation opportunities?
- Who will follow up on claims rejected for coding related issues?
- Who will monitor and be responsible for resolving pre-bill/ scrubber edits for rejected claims?

By this point, the educational basics and systems testing have been accomplished by studying the reimbursement impacts. A plan has been developed for continued coder and provider education and monitoring of productivity, documentation opportunities, as well as pre-bill edits, which may affect the revenue cycle.

1. Monitor Internal Editing and Quality Issues

Intensive continuous monitoring of both software and interface issues and the pre-bill/scrubber edits to facilitate timely revenue cycle is critical. Reports generated by patient financial services should be provided to the HIM department on a daily basis to allow the coding staff to evaluate the edits generated via the billing process. Such reports will assist in identifying any systematic errors or additional training needs.

2. Conduct Weekly Status Meetings

A weekly assessment meeting with coding leadership, project staff, and IS resources to address software/interface issues is required. Weekly meeting agenda topics should include the assessment of weak points and facilitate resolutions for productivity, software, interface, and quality as well as billing/edit issues. Identifying and addressing issues will be crucial to an uninterrupted billing cycle.

3. Provide Ongoing Feedback to Coding and Physician Staff

Education of coding professionals and patient care providers will be an ongoing process—especially regarding documentation, which is usually one of the weakest areas. Providing moral support and guidance to coding staff, answering questions, and resolving problems in an efficient manner will be required during the first few months after Go-Live to build confidence and mitigate coder anxiety.

Clinical Documentation Improvement Activities

ACTION STEPS

1. Support Clinicians through Training
2. Support Clinical Documentation Improvement Specialists

The relationship between clinical coding and clinical source documentation within the health record will affect every aspect of implementing ICD-10-CM/PCS. Providing education and raising awareness before the ICD-10-CM implementation date are the best approaches to improve documentation. It will be important to engage patient care providers, who typically have very tight appointment schedules, and to give them recognition for the important role they will play in a successful transition.

1. Support Clinicians through Training

The ICD-10-CM/PCS education provided documentation to help patient care providers understand the differences between ICD-10-CM/PCS and ICD-9-CM. The physicians will now be trained from applying the enhancements through influencing the documentation practices. One of the best ways to engage physicians is to create a support system that benefits the services they provide to patients. For instance, assisting in one-on-one or small practice group training sessions or creating smart text for electronic health records (EHRs) builds physician confidence in the new technology. This further allows the physician to spend more time with the patient instead of entering data into the EHR. Relate any documentation improvement approaches to the physician, and demonstrate different uses of clinical documentation other than coding for reimbursement. For instance, you may wish to provide physician profiles based on severity of illness and risk of mortality data, which are derived based on clinical documentation. Show how the newly implemented and enhanced technology will better serve the practice management through improved clinical data for mining, which may benefit any pay-for-performance initiatives, standard-of-care or quality programs, and payer contracts. If the physician enlists allied healthcare providers—such as physician assistants or certified nurse practitioners—for creating clinical documentation, it is important that they have been equally educated on the differences. The allied healthcare providers may be your first education link to the physician.

2. Support Clinical Documentation Improvement Specialists

If the facility has a CDI program, the staff has received comprehensive training in the differences between ICD-9-CM and ICD-10-CM and the enhanced specificity requirements. Be sure to support the CDI and ancillary department staff during Go-Live with a designated coding expert resource to answer any questions that may lessen the number of postdischarge queries. Using CDI specialists to reduce the incidence of physician postdischarge diagnostic specificity queries brought on by the enhanced ICD-10-CM coding system also will help further engage the physician during transition.

Post-Implementation

The implementation activities have been completed, but the project work is not finished. Post Go-Live will most likely include extensive issue resolution with software functionality and configurations that were inadvertently missed during the testing and Go-Live preparation activities. The project team should also review the lessons learned from the project to provide all parties involved with an opportunity for additional educational opportunities. This chapter discusses strategies to resolve post Go-Live issues, review the project, and learn from all activities completed, as well as plan for future changes that will come from payers as they collect enough data to base claims directly on ICD-10-CM/PCS codes instead of mapping them to ICD-9-CM codes for payment adjudication.

Organization-wide Implementation Project Review

ACTION STEPS

1. Identify Go-Live Issue Resolution Activities
2. Summarize Project Results
3. Evaluate Success Against Established Criteria
4. Identify the Key Lessons Learned
5. Assess the Project for Future Improvement
6. Celebrate Success
7. Plan for Next Steps with Payers

With the major work of the project behind you, the post Go-Live activities will initially include significant issue resolution. The first steps will be to resolve issues as quickly as possible, then take some time to reflect upon how your organization managed this project and successfully integrated ICD-10-CM/PCS into your claims processing activities. Finally, the entire transition process will not be complete until payers have modified their claim adjudication process to pay based on ICD-10-CM/PCS codes directly, which may come months or years post Go-Live. The project team needs to plan for these future activities in case the existing testing systems are required for participation in additional testing when these transitions occur.

1. Identify Go-Live Issue Resolution Activities

The complexity of this project is bound to result in issues post Go-Live. Having a plan to mitigate these issues and resolve them as quickly as possible is the best preparation strategy. The same process used during Go-Live preparation needs to be in place post Go-Live; the challenge will be in scheduling resources both internally and with vendors to resolve issues. Vendors will be extremely busy supporting all their clients. As we discussed previously, this is the largest transition the healthcare industry has ever been through in the history of the United States. Issues at Go-Live that result in facilities unable to be paid for any reason can result in a financial crisis. This type of crisis has happened in the past with implementation of regulatory requirements. The best means to avoid a crisis is to mitigate the risk by comprehensively testing the systems and links for the payment process; however, your organization can only be responsible for one side of the scenario. Vendors can very easily become overwhelmed with issues identified by their clients; after all, they may not have experienced all their clients going live with new functionality on the same day previously and may not have planned accordingly. Organizations should have some financial reserves in place in preparation for issues with specific payers.

2. Summarize Project Results

A project of this scale surely required resources to devote additional time and responsibilities over and above their daily roles. Now that the implementation is complete, most are ready to begin the next project. However, before the project team moves on to other activities, the project results should be revisited. This activity will include all team members, as the entire organization took part in the project, and should reflect on the following areas:

- Aspects of the project that went well
- Aspects of the project that could have been improved (including suggestions for improvement)
- Suggestions for additional roles, activities, or processes that could be incorporated into future projects

The most professional way to debrief a project is to provide each team member with an agenda and guide. Solicit opinions on what went exceptionally well and what was frustrating. To ensure that this exercise is a positive experience, it is strongly suggested that the project leadership team take into careful consideration how information is presented and discussed during this process. The project review meeting is not intended to become a complaint session to vent frustrations; instead, it should be a means for the organization to learn from the activities and grow.

3. Evaluate Success Against Established Criteria

As described in chapter 1, in the initial phases of the project the leadership team identified criteria for a successful project. These criteria included the expected outcomes of communication plans, Go-Live preparation activities, testing results, and vendor contract agreements. The criteria for success will vary depending on each facility; however, the evaluation list may include the following areas:

- Completion of assessment activities to identify required modifications
- Negotiation with software vendors to update contracts
- Coordination with payer agencies and coordinated testing activities
- Integration of project tasks across departments within the facility

There can be many components to the list and the key point is to recognize the areas in which you did well. Give public recognition to individuals who completed project activities while displaying exceptional leadership.

4. Identify the Key Lessons Learned

While identifying all the areas in which your team excelled and celebrating the success of the project, you should also identify the key lessons learned during the project. Some lessons were learned quickly while others may have been a result of trial and error. In either case, out of every issue comes an opportunity to learn from mistakes. Some lessons learned may include the following:

- Contractor X's work is superior and he (or she) should be contracted again for projects within the organization
- E-mail is not always the best means to communicate with team members. Instead, more use of phone calls, texting, or publishing information to the intranet is warranted
- Short daily meetings were a productive use of time during critical testing and Go–Live preparation activities
- Periodic, scheduled communications to the steering committee and project stakeholders were effective in mitigating end-user concerns

Lessons learned should be incorporated into future projects managed by your organization. The information gained during this debriefing process is important to identify potential future issues that could result in financial problems. When key staff resources leave an organization, their knowledge typically leaves with them. Take the time to document your lessons learned and project successes so resources throughout your organization have access to the knowledge gained during this enormous project.

5. Assess the Project for Future Improvement

Once you have reviewed the project activities, evaluate the overall project. How did the organization do in this process? Did you identify any areas you can improve at a higher level than the scope of the project? Could you benefit long-term from changes identified, acted upon, or discussed throughout the project? Looking at the project overall and how your organization handled such an undertaking will benefit your organization as a whole today and also on future projects. As the use of technology continues to grow, projects with similar levels of complexity will become more and more routine. Organizations that take the time to recognize opportunities to improve operations will experience positive results moving forward.

6. Celebrate Success

The last step is to celebrate the success of the project! The entire team deserves congratulations as the tasks completed over the course of the project were no small feat. This project was unlike any other and has changed not only your organization but the healthcare industry more significantly than anything in the past. For this achievement, all team members should be proud of the work they have accomplished, and the facility should be pleased that the initial hard work is complete. Just as important as evaluating the project, it is important to celebrate the work, and every organization should take some time to recognize the project team and the work you have accomplished.

7. Plan for Next Steps with Payers

Payers are all planning to collect ICD-10-CM/PCS codes and map them back to the ICD-9-CM payment rates for an undetermined period of time. CMS most likely will take two years to collect data from the updated code set prior to changing payment based on ICD-10-CM/PCS codes; however, the time payers take to pay is not part of the regulation and therefore payers can take as much time as they choose. Most likely, the large payers will follow a similar timeframe to what CMS is using, but every payer will be looking to make changes at some point in the future. Organizations need to be aware of this future change and plan appropriately for the changes. More information will be determined as time of the implementation becomes closer; at the time of this publication, issues such as this are being discussed and are still unclear. Organizations should work closely with payers throughout the implementation process and remember that the work with these vendors is not done at Go-Live as it will be for some vendors. The work with the payers will most likely continue through the resources within Patient Financial Services; however, changes should be communicated with IS and HIM as they are required.

Information Systems Post-Implementation Activities

ACTION STEPS

1. Resolve Outstanding Issues
2. Summarize Project Results
3. Evaluate the Vendors
4. Work with IS to Manage Increased Data Flow
5. Legacy Software Systems and Databases

The IS department's technology modifications plan included expected outcomes for each software system throughout the course of this project. Once post Go-Live issues have been resolved, expected outcomes identified by the project team can be evaluated. The project team should review the expected outcomes to determine if the outcome of each activity, including project successes, key lessons learned, and activities to manage the new data elements included in the expanded ICD-10-CM/PCS code set within your systems inventory, was successful as a result of the project.

1. Resolve Outstanding Issues

Issues identified should be documented and communicated to the vendor as quickly and seamlessly as possible. Dedicated resources should be responsible for capturing the issue details and communicating them to the designated internal team member. The project team should continue to meet on a regular basis until all issues have been resolved and no new issues have been identified for a designated period of time. Because issues will arise post Go-Live and will need to be a part of the routine management of the applications, the minimum time identified should be 30 days. Post Go-Live issues tend to be more significant and a direct result of the Go-Live event, requiring additional resources to assist in the resolution process. Once the team has disbanded as a result of formally ending the project, it will be difficult to rally them back together to test and validate additional issues and modifications. Therefore, make sure you don't need their dedicated services and participation in the project prior to disbanding the team.

2. Summarize Project Results

Implementing ICD-10-CM/PCS significantly changes your organization's software systems. The results of your project work included a successful implementation and transmission of a completely new code set and claims processing format. Data elements within the software structures that were changed may have resulted in operational changes throughout your organization. Some of these changes could include new data elements to review on a regular basis, which would alter the standard reports regularly distributed and accessed before the Go-Live event. Such operational changes tend to grow as more and more resources see benefits from the enhanced code set. As a result, the IS department is typically just as busy with activities to support end-user requests post Go-Live as they were during the actual Go-Live activities. Nonetheless, it is important to review the project activities to identify the success criteria and key lessons learned and evaluate the tools used throughout the project. The IS project lead should thoroughly review the project, evaluating the results and success criteria. Each team member should have input in the evaluation process, and lessons learned should be incorporated into future IS projects. As the IS project team completes the evaluation activities, it is important to include the tools used during the project to evaluate the vendors and their associated software systems.

3. Evaluate the Vendors

At the start of the project, the IS team designed assessment questionnaires and tools to evaluate the current use of ICD-9-CM codes and new requirements to implement ICD-10-CM/PCS code sets. The team should take time to review each tool used and evaluate the following:

- Were the formats for the tools used during the project appropriate for the data necessary to be collected?
- Did the tools include the appropriate questions?
- What additional information should be included for a future project?
- Were the tools distributed to the appropriate resources?
- What additional tools should be developed for future projects?

The results of the project evaluation will assist the team members, as well as the organization, with future projects of any size.

4. Work with IS to Manage Increased Data Flow

The implementation of the ICD-10-CM/PCS code sets will ultimately increase the use of technology throughout your organization. As the daily activities become more systems oriented, operations ultimately change as the importance of electronic data management surpasses paper management. Many organizations identify new positions for data management used by the new and updated software systems. Reports produced from each application should be analyzed in accordance with the system modifications completed during the project activities. Before the Go-Live event, reports transmitting ICD-9-CM information may not be adequate to encompass data from ICD-10-CM/PCS and could therefore result in changes made to the existing reports. Due to the format of ICD-10-CM/PCS data, report formats may continue to evolve over time as more and more users use the broader code categories. The IS and HIM departments should work closely to monitor the data produced by the modified systems and to incorporate changes as needed and identified by end-users on a routine basis. A specific resource within your facility should be responsible for managing reports produced by each software system. Knowledgeable resources responsible for distributing the collected information are a vital role in the effective management of an electronic HIM environment.

5. Legacy Software Systems and Databases

Applications, systems, and databases that hold ICD-9-CM data will also need to be maintained for a period of time beyond Go-Live to accommodate claim adjudication, audits, research, and reporting activities of the organization. Legacy systems will have to be maintained and supported as well as modern historical applications. IS departments need to consider the long-term need for ICD-9-CM data within organizations and plan for need to not only reference but utilize the ICD-9-CM data on an ongoing basis. The data contained in legacy systems will not easily be converted to modern formats without extensive development and testing to ensure that the quality of historical data is maintained. Each organization will need to determine how to best handle historical data, including databases from vendors that are no longer supported post Go-Live. It is best if the long-term plan for legacy systems is included in the project plan to identify if project resources should be kept on the project post Go-Live to complete additional tasks necessary to deal with historical and legacy data.

Health Information Management Department
Post-Implementation Activities

ACTION STEPS

1. Benchmark and Review Specific Measures
2. Continue Quality Review Action Plan
3. Communicate Success and Provide Support

The HIM department's Go-Live plan included establishing pre-implementation status of important coding operations benchmarks and targets. It is important now for HIM to gather the essential post Go-Live ICD-10-CM/PCS data for comparison and to measure the coding staff's performance and improvement.

1. Benchmark and Review Specific Measures

As part of the implementation, the HIM coding manager developed an action plan for collecting post-implementation ICD-10-CM/PCS data for comparison to pre-implementation ICD-9-CM data. The information collected and reported should be shared transparently with the coding staff. Consider charting the following post-implementation data for comparison for each patient encounter type coded by the HIM department:

- Discharged, not final billed
- Coding team productivity
- Post-discharge query rate
- Failed claim rates
- Post-discharge query answer rate (includes average turnaround time)

These data should be shared on a regular basis with the organization-wide implementation team.

2. Continue Quality Review Action Plan

The HIM department plan includes performing ICD-10-CM/PCS quality reviews for educational purposes during and beyond Go-Live. Any established regular pre-implementation quality review activities should be continued and educational feedback provided to the coding staff. If available, benchmark activities using past ICD-9-CM quality statistics for each coder and team. Post-implementation, the coding manager should consider suspending any employee corrective action policies regarding quality expectations for at least six to nine months to allow for a reasonable learning curve. According to AHIMA previously conducted ICD-10-CM/PCS application studies, with the proper training, this should be enough time for the HIM professional coder to become proficient in applying ICD-10-CM/PCS.

Figures 4.1 and 4.2 show snapshots of sample inpatient and outpatient coding quality spreadsheets. The customizable files on the CD-ROM include embedded formulas for each patient type, which may be used for recording and reporting individual coding statistics. The spreadsheets provide a review mechanism to communicate the coder's ICD-10-CM/PCS quality statistics and to track improvement.

3. Communicate Success and Provide Support

It is important to communicate the HIM department's ICD-10-CM/PCS project successes facility-wide and to patient care providers. Any post-implementation coding support activities—such as a coding help desk or call line—provided to patient care providers, financial services, and ancillary department personnel should continue as long as needed until business functions return to acceptable, established pre-implementation targets.

Figure 4.1. Extract from inpatient coding quality review worksheet

Account No.	Discharge Date	MR #	DRG		Principal Dx		Secondary Dx		Principal Px		Secondary Px		POA Abstracting		Comments
			Correct	Total	Correct	Total	Correct	Total	Correct	Total	Correct	Total	Correct	Total	
1				1		1									
2				1		1									
3				1		1									
4				1		1									
5				1		1									
			0	25	0	25	0	0	0	0	0	0	0	0	

Figure 4.2. Extract from outpatient coding quality review worksheet

Patient Number	Date of Service	First Listed Dx		Secondary Dx		Comments
		Correct	Total	Correct	Total	
1			1			
2			1			
3			1			
4			1			
5			1			
		0	25	0	0	

Total Coding Accuracy Rate: **0.0%**

Ongoing Education of Coding Professionals

Education for coding staff during the post-implementation phase includes trending errors to enhance educational opportunities as well as improvement in coding quality and providing continuous feedback to the coding staff. Review clinical documentation on an ongoing basis and suggest areas of improvement. These efforts will allow for a decrease in coding errors as time progresses and ensure complete and accurate documentation at the time of discharge.

1. Document Educational Opportunities to Facilitate Ongoing Education of Coding Staff

The education process from this point on consists of monitoring productivity and commonly found errors, and identifying educational opportunities for the coding staff. Initially, all errors should be treated as though the entire coding staff is making them, as this may very well be the case. It is important to establish the most common areas in which errors are occurring. Reviewing these errors in a team meeting setting will generate discussions, promote education, and facilitate consistency among the coding staff. Maintain a Microsoft Excel® spreadsheet for each coder and overall coding section to track errors and develop educational materials. If your facility does not already have quality improvement worksheets, those shown in figures 4.1 and 4.2, which are included on the CD-ROM as Excel spreadsheets, can be customized for your facility. The forms incorporate account number, discharge date, medical record number, total ICD-10-CM/PCS codes, and number of errors in principal diagnosis/procedure, as well as secondary diagnosis/procedure codes. Formulas are incorporated in the worksheet to not only measure coding accuracy but also DRG accuracy for each coder.

Quality review should focus on educational opportunities. Use this information collected in the worksheet as a means of measuring each coder's performance improvement during the learning curve, which AHIMA estimates will take six to nine months. As time progresses and the coding staff members become more confident with the coding system, the Excel spreadsheet can be adapted to measure performance.

2. Provide Feedback for Educating Clinical Documentation Review Staff

In addition, continuous monitoring for improved documentation opportunities for concurrent review staff is required. Assuming the facility employs clinical or nursing staff for case management or utilization review, it is necessary for the coding staff to provide feedback to the concurrent reviewers to achieve the appropriate documentation required for the increased specificity in the ICD-10-CM coding system. Focusing efforts on communicating incomplete areas for code specificity will facilitate improvements at the time of discharge and complete and accurate diagnoses coding in both outpatient and inpatient stays. In addition, procedures during the inpatient stay may require concurrent follow-up for specificity. The ICD-10-CM/PCS coding system may require specialty providers to enhance documentation with code specificity.

3. Plan for Continuous Education of Physician/Provider Staff

If a concurrent program is not used for documentation improvement, physician and patient care provider education will require an ICD-10-CM/PCS speaker who has an established relationship with the clinicians. Increased queries after patient discharge are not efficient or beneficial to the revenue cycle. In addition, physicians may be reticent about adding documentation to the health record after a patient is discharged. The benefits of addressing the documentation issues proactively far outweigh the disadvantages. Refer to the talking points for healthcare providers in appendix 2.2 for suggested topics to present for speaking opportunities, and newsletters or bulletins to provide to the medical staff. As much personal interaction as possible with medical staff members is advantageous because members may overlook the newsletters or bulletins communication formats.

Limit each bulletin to one or two significant areas of documentation improvement. Focus on the benefits of improving documentation to improve severity of illness for profiling and patient outcomes management. While hospital finance is not usually of interest to the medical staff, profiling of patients' severity of illness and risk of mortality and documentation affecting patient outcomes directly impacts physician acuity and outcome data and can make a difference not only in improving patient care, but also in managed care contract negotiations and pay for performance.

Ongoing Clinical Documentation Improvement Activities

ACTION STEPS

1. Plan for Ongoing Assessment
2. Develop an Action Plan

Clinical documentation is and always will be the basis for accuracy in coding and reporting patient encounters. Throughout the ICD-10-CM/PCS implementation process and beyond, continuous improvement of clinical documentation will remain the most important element for accurate reporting and reimbursement.

1. Plan for Ongoing Assessment

Post-implementation is the perfect time to continue the momentum for making clinical documentation improvement (CDI) a priority. The focus of change to the new code set has brought awareness to everyone within the organization. Use the opportunity to capitalize on the benefits that increased statistical data can provide to the business of healthcare. Develop a plan for continual auditing and assessing clinical documentation. For instance, as you quantify the queries submitted by the coding staff during post-implementation activities, also quantify the queries by disease or procedure category. Share this information with your physician leadership team, and brainstorm for improving documentation methods to include the required increased specificity. ICD-10-PCS offers an ideal opportunity to improve computer-assisted procedural documentation choices within the electronic health record. Patient care providers will be in favor of these improvements because they will serve to decrease the time spent to document encounters. In addition, clinical documentation forms review should be a part of the assessment plan.

2. Develop an Action Plan

Build an action plan to continue the momentum of CDI throughout the facility. For instance, each time an area of CDI is identified in data collection, convene a group of key stakeholders to create and enact solutions on a fast track. Tackling small areas for improvement one at a time can create confidence among staff members. In order to be successful, the action plan should be based on the size of the practice, department, or service area. Each CDI area identified may require a different approach. This designer approach system may seem difficult at first, but as it progresses, you will quickly be able to ascertain the best practices for obtaining the desired results. There is no one correct action plan—it is whatever solution works to get patient care provider buy-in and improvement for the organization. Remember to provide public recognition to the physician and allied health providers for their cooperation in CDI produced by the action plan.

Positive Changes in the United States Healthcare System

General Benefits

Many articles have been written regarding the positive changes to the healthcare system and data enrichment as a result of implementing ICD-10-CM/PCS. Overall, the benefits of the specificity contained within ICD-10-CM/PCS are obvious—richer data for appropriate reimbursement, pay-for-performance (P4P) quality initiatives, and research. The more immediate challenge is that the ICD-9-CM coding system will soon be out of fields to accommodate new diagnoses, thus compromising reimbursement to providers, international health data, provider profiling, and research outcome data. Implementing ICD-10-CM/PCS will significantly improve data integrity and allow the U.S. healthcare system to align health data with other countries on a global basis, as most of the developed countries have been utilizing ICD-10 for many years to classify disease processes for morbidity and mortality of their patient population.

Public Health and Global Implications

The World Health Organization (WHO), of which the United States is a member, maintains the International Classification of Diseases (ICD), which is now in the tenth revision. The United States maintains a Clinical Modification—that is, ICD-10-CM—for the classification of diseases for research, quality, and reimbursement purposes. The WHO Web site (2009) states the following:

> The ICD is the international standard diagnostic classification for all general epidemiological, many health

CHAPTER 5

157

management purposes and clinical use. These include the analysis of the general health situation of population groups and monitoring of the incidence and prevalence of diseases and other health problems in relation to other variables such as the characteristics and circumstances of the individuals affected, reimbursement, resource allocation, quality and guidelines. It is used to classify diseases and other health problems recorded on many types of health and vital records including death certificates and health records. In addition to enabling the storage and retrieval of diagnostic information for clinical, epidemiological and quality purposes, these records also provide the basis for the compilation of national mortality and morbidity statistics by WHO Member States.

The importance of being able to share health data internationally for rapid detection of communicable diseases cannot be understated and as Bowman writes (2008, 24):

> The United States is the only industrialized nation not using an ICD-10 based classification system for morbidity purposes. This makes it difficult to share disease data internationally at a time when such sharing is critical for the public health. The vision is that every country should be able to detect, rapidly verify, and respond appropriately to epidemic-prone and emerging disease threats to minimize their impact on the health and economy of the world's population. Adoption of ICD-10-CM also would facilitate international comparisons of quality of care and the sharing of best practices globally.

A common language as a basis to link healthcare knowledge globally is required to effectively communicate disease processes as well as efficacy in patient treatment modalities and outcome data. The specificity in ICD-10 facilitates effective communication of reportable diseases such as AIDS and organism-specific epidemics throughout the world. Keckley, as quoted in Chavis 2008 (20), states:

> 'The health of populations supersedes country borders, so it is logical that knowledge about these diseases, their causes and cures, should be an international pursuit void of political boundaries and bias,' says Paul H. Keckley, PhD, executive director at the Deloitte Center for Health Solutions. 'ICD-10 is, in many ways, a highway for international collaboration, a common language already spoken by 10 countries.

The ability to compare critical healthcare data on a global basis is essential to tracking specific infectious disease processes or bio-terrorism events. A 2009 AHIMA report found that:

> Replacing ICD-9-CM with ICD-10-CM will better maintain clinical data comparability with the rest of the world concerning the conditions prompting healthcare services. ICD-10 will make it easier to share disease and mortality data at the time when such global data sharing is critical for public health. For example:
> - ICD-10-CM would have better documented the West Nile Virus and SARS complexes for earlier detection and better tracking
> - ICD-10-CM also provides the ability to track bio-terrorism events and other public health outbreaks.

Research

For decades, coded clinical data has been increasingly used by Centers for Medicare & Medicaid Services (CMS) and other regulatory agencies for myriad quality-of-care improvement and pay for performance (P4P) initiatives, utilization and outcome studies, and setting healthcare policy The findings drive provider reimbursement and are critical to improving patient care and clinical efficiency initiatives.

The increased specificity and granularity of ICD-10-CM/PCS allow for improved disease management, better understanding of healthcare outcomes, and appropriate reimbursement for new procedures and disease processes. An example of improved outcome would be decubitus ulcers. Currently in the ICD-9-CM classification system, two codes are required to delineate site and stage of the ulcers. In ICD-10-CM, only one code is required to delineate both site and stage of the ulcer. In the ICD-9-CM classification, there is potential for the second code delineating stage of the ulcer to be dropped from the top nine diagnoses currently reported to CMS for reimbursement and other studies if the patient has other comorbid or complicating diagnoses. If the decubitus ulcer is Stage IV with necrosis to the bone and the bone is debrided during the stay, the procedure code reflects a bone debridement for a decubitus ulcer. Quality edits may flag these codes as the procedure being inconsistent with diagnosis provided for billing. In addition, outcomes and resource utilization may also be reflected as being disproportionate to care actually provided. This example is just one of many demonstrating how ICD-10-CM will improve reflection of clinical outcomes and resource utilization.

Global implications are significant as the greater detail of ICD-10-CM/PCS allows for worldwide uniformity of managing clinical trials, outcomes, and epidemic studies performed.

Reimbursement

Reimbursement implications are significant with the transition to ICD-10-CM/PCS because it allows for clearer alignment of services to conditions treated. Thus, reimbursement is more in line with services rendered during the patient stay. ICD-9-CM was developed as a classification system, without consideration to reimbursement. ICD-10-CM/PCS lends itself to be easily revised and expanded as new clinical conditions, technologies, and procedures are identified and developed. This greater detail assists with increased accuracy in coding and more appropriate reimbursement for treatments provided.

Fraud and abuse can be more effectively identified as ICD-10-CM/PCS is more specific and has fewer ambiguities than ICD-9-CM. According to Bowman (2008, 24):

> Greater detail may lead to better justification of medical necessity and improved implementation of national and local coverage determinations. With continued use of ICD-9-CM, conditions that support medical necessity for a particular service may be classified to the same code as conditions that would not justify the service.

Coding errors are a focus of CMS related to fraud and abuse and are monitored and measured by QIOs, RAC auditors and many other entities that report potential reimbursement discrepancies related to these errors. Eliminating the risk of these errors continues to be a primary focus. Libicki and Brahmakulam state (2004):

> It is anticipated that implementation of ICD-10-CM and -PCS will ultimately result in a lower coding error rate than ICD-9-CM and fewer erroneous and rejected reimbursement claims because these systems are less ambiguous and more logically organized and detailed.

Timely turnaround and fewer rejections of claims will be the primary focus of providers to maintain cash flow during and following the transition. After the initial learning curve—which AHIMA estimates at six to nine months for experienced coders, the degree of specificity and logic in ICD-10-CM/PCS logic lends to greater accuracy when interpreting clinical documentation. Quality information provided in the patient record makes code selection more precise.

As medical advances continue, public reporting of quality indicators is expected to become more prevalent, with greater emphasis placed on payment for quality. Detailed and accurate information is essential for good reporting (HFMA 2004, 1).

References

AHIMA. 2009. Why ICD-9-CM is Being Replaced. http://www.ahima.org/
icd10/icd9.asp.

Bowman, S. 2008. Why ICD-10 Is Worth the Trouble. *Journal of AHIMA*
79(3):24–29.

Chavis, Selena. Crossing Over to ICD-10. *For The Record* 20(24):20.

Libicki, M and Brahmakulam, I. 2004. The Costs and Benefits of Moving to
the ICD-10 Code Sets. RAND Corporation. http://www.rand.org/pubs/
technical_reports/2004/RAND_TR132.pdf.

Healthcare Financial Management Association. 2004. ICD-10: Capturing the Complexities of Health Care. http://www.hfma.org/NR/
rdonlyres/D915857C-FC28-4D11-9BDF-527B5C55B989/0/HFMA_
ICD10_200404_6.pdf.

World Health Organization Classification Web site, http://www.who.int/
classifications/icd/en/.

ICD-10 Implementation Schedule

The implementation schedule is a template to use in organizing and building an enterprise project schedule to implement ICD-10-CM/PCS. The project team should expand, modify, and delete the details to include all tasks and milestones necessary to be completed throughout the project duration specific to your project. In order to display the project schedule, some columns have been hidden from view. The full Microsoft project file can be found on the CD-ROM. Generic resources have been included in the template. Once the work breakdown structure has been completed and project tasks have been assigned, specific resources can be added to the project schedule and linked to tasks.

ID	●	Task Name	Duration	Start	Finish	Resource Names
1		**ICD-10 Implementation Schedule**	**1353 days**	**Fri 1/16/09**	**Tue 3/25/14**	**Executive Sponsor**
2		**Final Regulations**	**792 days**	**Fri 1/16/09**	**Mon 1/30/12**	**Health and Human Services**
3	📅📅	Published Rule - ICD-10, v5010, vD.0 and v.3.0	1 day	Fri 1/16/09	Fri 1/16/09	CMS
4	📅📅	Rule effective	1 day	Tue 3/17/09	Tue 3/17/09	CMS
5		**Version 5010/D.0/3.0 Activities**	**542 days**	**Fri 1/1/10**	**Mon 1/30/12**	**Steering Committee**
6	📅	Begin Internal Testing for Versions 5010, D.0 and 3.0	239 days	Fri 1/1/10	Wed 12/1/10	Core Project Team
7		Complete Level 1 Compliance for Versions 5010, D.0 and 3.0	20 days	Thu 12/2/10	Wed 12/29/10	Core Project Team
8	📅	Begin External Testing for Versions 5010, D.0 and 3.0	261 days	Mon 1/3/11	Mon 1/2/12	Core Project Team
9		Complete Level 2 Compliance for Versions 5010, D.0 and 3.0	20 days	Tue 1/3/12	Mon 1/30/12	Core Project Team
10		**Planning**	**62 days**	**Mon 6/1/09**	**Tue 8/25/09**	**Steering Committee**
11	📅	Kick-off Meeting	1 day	Mon 6/1/09	Mon 6/1/09	Sponsor,Core Project Team,Steering Committee
12		**Develop Project Documents**	**50 days**	**Tue 6/2/09**	**Mon 8/10/09**	**Steering Committee**
13		Work Breakdown Schedule (WBS)	15 days	Tue 6/2/09	Mon 6/22/09	Core Project Team
14		**Project Strategy**	**5 days**	**Tue 6/23/09**	**Mon 6/29/09**	**Steering Committee**
18		Project Budget	15 days	Tue 6/30/09	Mon 7/20/09	Steering Committee
19		Project Schedule and Plan	15 days	Tue 7/21/09	Mon 8/10/09	Project Manager
20		**Submit Project Documents for Approval**	**36 days**	**Tue 6/23/09**	**Tue 8/11/09**	**Steering Committee**
21		Work Breakdown Schedule (WBS)	1 day	Tue 6/23/09	Tue 6/23/09	Core Project Team
22		Project Strategy	1 day	Tue 6/30/09	Tue 6/30/09	Steering Committee
23		Project Budget	1 day	Tue 7/21/09	Tue 7/21/09	Steering Committee
24		Project Schedule and Plan	1 day	Tue 8/11/09	Tue 8/11/09	Project Manager
25		**Approve Project Documents**	**45 days**	**Wed 6/24/09**	**Tue 8/25/09**	**Steering Committee**
26		Work Breakdown Schedule (WBS)	10 days	Wed 6/24/09	Tue 7/7/09	Project Manager
27		Project Strategy	10 days	Wed 7/1/09	Tue 7/14/09	Steering Committee
28		Project Budget	10 days	Wed 7/22/09	Tue 8/4/09	Steering Committee
29		Project Schedule and Plan	10 days	Wed 8/12/09	Tue 8/25/09	Steering Committee
30	⟳	**Communication Management**	**1023 days**	**Wed 1/6/10**	**Fri 12/6/13**	**Steering Committee**
31	⟳	Steering Committee Status Meetings	1001 days	Fri 2/5/10	Fri 12/6/13	Steering Committee
79	⟳	Core Project Team Status Meeting	981 days	Wed 1/6/10	Wed 10/9/13	Core Project Team
277	⟳	**Outreach Communications**	**481 days**	**Mon 1/2/12**	**Mon 11/4/13**	**Executive Sponsor**
301		**Impact Assessment (Gap Analysis)**	**60 days**	**Wed 8/26/09**	**Tue 11/17/09**	**Steering Committee**
302		**Develop Assessment Questionnaires**	**20 days**	**Wed 8/26/09**	**Tue 9/22/09**	**Project Manager**
303		HIM Process	20 days	Wed 8/26/09	Tue 9/22/09	HIM Project Team
304		IT/Systems	20 days	Wed 8/26/09	Tue 9/22/09	IT Project Team
305		Coding Training	20 days	Wed 8/26/09	Tue 9/22/09	HIM Project Team
306		Clinical Documentation Improvement	10 days	Wed 8/26/09	Tue 9/8/09	HIM Project Team
307		**Distribute Assessment Questionnaires**	**40 days**	**Wed 9/23/09**	**Tue 11/17/09**	**Project Manager**
308		Pt. Access/Admitting	5 days	Wed 9/23/09	Tue 9/29/09	HIM Project Lead
309		HIM/HIS	5 days	Wed 9/30/09	Tue 10/6/09	HIM Project Lead
310		Clinical Teams	5 days	Wed 10/7/09	Tue 10/13/09	HIM Project Lead
311		Medical Staff	5 days	Wed 10/14/09	Tue 10/20/09	HIM Project Lead
312		IT/Systems - Internal	10 days	Wed 10/21/09	Tue 11/3/09	IT Project Lead
313		Vendors	10 days	Wed 11/4/09	Tue 11/17/09	IT Project Lead
314		**Implementation (Design)**	**535 days**	**Wed 9/30/09**	**Tue 10/18/11**	**Steering Committee**
315		**Collect Assessment Questionnaires**	**55 days**	**Wed 9/30/09**	**Tue 12/15/09**	**Project Manager**

ID	❶	Task Name	Duration	Start	Finish	Resource Names
316		Pt. Access/Admitting	10 days	Wed 9/30/09	Tue 10/13/09	HIM Project Team
317		HIM/HIS	10 days	Wed 10/14/09	Tue 10/27/09	HIM Project Team
318		Clinical Teams	10 days	Wed 10/28/09	Tue 11/10/09	HIM Project Team
319		Medical Staff	10 days	Wed 11/11/09	Tue 11/24/09	HIM Project Team
320		IT/Systems - Internal	15 days	Wed 11/4/09	Tue 11/24/09	IT Project Team
321		Vendors	15 days	Wed 11/25/09	Tue 12/15/09	IT Project Team
322		**Analyze Results & Develop Action Plan**	**135 days**	**Wed 10/14/09**	**Tue 4/20/10**	**Project Manager**
323		Pt. Access/Admitting	45 days	Wed 10/14/09	Tue 12/15/09	HIM Project Team
324		HIM/HIS	45 days	Wed 10/28/09	Tue 12/29/09	HIM Project Team
325		Clinical Teams	45 days	Wed 11/11/09	Tue 1/12/10	HIM Project Team
326		Medical Staff	45 days	Wed 11/25/09	Tue 1/26/10	HIM Project Team
327		IT/Systems - Internal and Vendor	90 days	Wed 11/25/09	Tue 3/30/10	IT Project Team
328		IT/Systems - External	90 days	Wed 12/16/09	Tue 4/20/10	IT Project Team
329		**Software System Replacement Process**	**390 days**	**Wed 4/21/10**	**Tue 10/18/11**	**Project Manager**
330		Vendor Identification	60 days	Wed 4/21/10	Tue 7/13/10	Core Project Team
331		Software System Functional Evaluation and Comparison	120 days	Wed 7/14/10	Tue 12/28/10	Core Project Team
332		Final Vendor Selection	90 days	Wed 12/29/10	Tue 5/3/11	Core Project Team
333		Contract Negotiation	120 days	Wed 5/4/11	Tue 10/18/11	Core Project Team
334		**Go-Live Preparation (Development and Testing)**	**915 days**	**Wed 4/21/10**	**Tue 10/22/13**	**Steering Committee**
335		Develop Go-Live Plan	30 days	Wed 5/4/11	Tue 6/14/11	Project Manager
336		Distribute Go-Live Plan	1 day	Wed 6/15/11	Wed 6/15/11	Project Manager
337		**Execute Project Plans**	**898 days**	**Wed 4/21/10**	**Fri 9/27/13**	**Project Manager**
338		**Initial ICD-10-CM and ICD-10-PCS Training and Education**	**60 days**	**Thu 6/16/11**	**Wed 9/7/11**	**HIM Project Lead**
339		Clinical Staff	15 days	Thu 6/16/11	Wed 7/6/11	HIM Project Team
340		Medical Staff	15 days	Thu 7/7/11	Wed 7/27/11	HIM Project Team
341		Billing/Financial Staff	15 days	Thu 7/28/11	Wed 8/17/11	HIM Project Team
342		HIM/Coding Staff	15 days	Thu 8/18/11	Wed 9/7/11	HIM Project Team
343		**Internal Software System Modifications**	**360 days**	**Thu 9/8/11**	**Wed 1/23/13**	**IT Project Lead**
344		**Update Vendor/Contractor Contracts**	**60 days**	**Thu 9/8/11**	**Wed 11/30/11**	**IT Project Lead,HIM Project Lead**
345		Clinical Systems	60 days	Thu 9/8/11	Wed 11/30/11	IT Project Lead
346		Coding Systems	60 days	Thu 9/8/11	Wed 11/30/11	HIM Project Lead
347		Payment Systems	60 days	Thu 9/8/11	Wed 11/30/11	IT Project Lead
348		**Implement Test Systems**	**90 days**	**Thu 12/1/11**	**Wed 4/4/12**	**IT Project Lead,HIM Project Lead**
349		Clinical Systems	90 days	Thu 12/1/11	Wed 4/4/12	IT Project Lead
350		Coding Systems	90 days	Thu 12/1/11	Wed 4/4/12	HIM Project Lead
351		Payment Systems	90 days	Thu 12/1/11	Wed 4/4/12	IT Project Lead
352		Complete System Training	60 days	Thu 4/5/12	Wed 6/27/12	Core Project Team
353		**Design System Modification to Accommodate ICD-10 Codes**	**90 days**	**Thu 6/28/12**	**Wed 10/31/12**	**IT Project Lead,HIM Project Lead**
354		Clinical Systems	90 days	Thu 6/28/12	Wed 10/31/12	IT Project Team
355		Coding Systems	90 days	Thu 6/28/12	Wed 10/31/12	HIM Project Team
356		Payment Systems	90 days	Thu 6/28/12	Wed 10/31/12	IT Project Team
357		**Complete System Modifications**	**60 days**	**Thu 11/1/12**	**Wed 1/23/13**	**IT Project Lead,HIM Project Lead**
358		Clinical Systems	60 days	Thu 11/1/12	Wed 1/23/13	IT Project Team
359		Coding Systems	60 days	Thu 11/1/12	Wed 1/23/13	HIM Project Team
360		Payment Systems	60 days	Thu 11/1/12	Wed 1/23/13	IT Project Team

ID	o	Task Name	Duration	Start	Finish	Resource Names
361		**Internal System Testing and Validation**	**110 days**	**Thu 1/24/13**	**Wed 6/26/13**	**IT Project Lead**
362		**Develop Testing Plan**	**20 days**	**Thu 1/24/13**	**Wed 2/20/13**	**IT Project Lead,HIM Project Lead**
363		Clinical Systems	20 days	Thu 1/24/13	Wed 2/20/13	IT Project Team
364		Coding Systems	20 days	Thu 1/24/13	Wed 2/20/13	HIM Project Team
365		Payment Systems	20 days	Thu 1/24/13	Wed 2/20/13	IT Project Team
366		**Complete Testing Steps**	**45 days**	**Thu 2/21/13**	**Wed 4/24/13**	**IT Project Lead,HIM Project Lead**
367		Clinical Systems	45 days	Thu 2/21/13	Wed 4/24/13	IT Project Team
368		Coding Systems	45 days	Thu 2/21/13	Wed 4/24/13	HIM Project Team
369		Payment Systems	45 days	Thu 2/21/13	Wed 4/24/13	IT Project Team
370		**Complete Validation Steps**	**45 days**	**Thu 4/25/13**	**Wed 6/26/13**	**IT Project Lead,HIM Project Lead**
371		Clinical Systems	45 days	Thu 4/25/13	Wed 6/26/13	IT Project Team
372		Coding Systems	45 days	Thu 4/25/13	Wed 6/26/13	HIM Project Team
373		Payment Systems	45 days	Thu 4/25/13	Wed 6/26/13	IT Project Team
374		**External Software System Modifications**	**420 days**	**Wed 4/21/10**	**Tue 11/29/11**	**IT Project Lead**
375		**Update Vendor/Contractor Contracts**	**60 days**	**Wed 4/21/10**	**Tue 7/13/10**	**IT Project Lead,HIM Project Lead**
376		Clinical Systems	60 days	Wed 4/21/10	Tue 7/13/10	IT Project Lead
377		Coding Systems	60 days	Wed 4/21/10	Tue 7/13/10	HIM Project Lead
378		Payment Systems	60 days	Wed 4/21/10	Tue 7/13/10	IT Project Lead
379		**Implement Test Systems**	**60 days**	**Wed 7/14/10**	**Tue 10/5/10**	**IT Project Lead,HIM Project Lead**
380		Clinical Systems	60 days	Wed 7/14/10	Tue 10/5/10	IT Project Lead
381		Coding Systems	60 days	Wed 7/14/10	Tue 10/5/10	HIM Project Lead
382		Payment Systems	60 days	Wed 7/14/10	Tue 10/5/10	IT Project Lead
383		Complete System Training	60 days	Wed 10/6/10	Tue 12/28/10	Core Project Team
384		**Design System Modification to Accommodate ICD-10 Codes**	**90 days**	**Wed 12/29/10**	**Tue 5/3/11**	**IT Project Lead,HIM Project Lead**
385		Clinical Systems	90 days	Wed 12/29/10	Tue 5/3/11	IT Project Team
386		Coding Systems	90 days	Wed 12/29/10	Tue 5/3/11	HIM Project Team
387		Payment Systems	90 days	Wed 12/29/10	Tue 5/3/11	IT Project Team
388		**Complete System Modifications**	**150 days**	**Wed 5/4/11**	**Tue 11/29/11**	**IT Project Lead,HIM Project Lead**
389		Clinical Systems	150 days	Wed 5/4/11	Tue 11/29/11	IT Project Team
390		Coding Systems	150 days	Wed 5/4/11	Tue 11/29/11	HIM Project Team
391		Payment Systems	150 days	Wed 5/4/11	Tue 11/29/11	IT Project Team
392		**External System Testing and Validation**	**370 days**	**Wed 11/30/11**	**Tue 4/30/13**	**IT Project Lead**
393		**Develop Testing Plan**	**120 days**	**Wed 11/30/11**	**Tue 5/15/12**	**IT Project Lead,HIM Project Lead**
394		Clinical Systems	120 days	Wed 11/30/11	Tue 5/15/12	IT Project Team
395		Coding Systems	120 days	Wed 11/30/11	Tue 5/15/12	HIM Project Team
396		Payment Systems	120 days	Wed 11/30/11	Tue 5/15/12	IT Project Team
397		**Complete Testing Steps**	**130 days**	**Wed 5/16/12**	**Tue 11/13/12**	**IT Project Lead,HIM Project Lead**
398		Clinical Systems	130 days	Wed 5/16/12	Tue 11/13/12	IT Project Team
399		Coding Systems	130 days	Wed 5/16/12	Tue 11/13/12	HIM Project Team
400		Payment Systems	130 days	Wed 5/16/12	Tue 11/13/12	IT Project Team
401		**Complete Validation Steps**	**120 days**	**Wed 11/14/12**	**Tue 4/30/13**	**IT Project Lead,HIM Project Lead**
402		Clinical Systems	120 days	Wed 11/14/12	Tue 4/30/13	IT Project Team
403		Coding Systems	120 days	Wed 11/14/12	Tue 4/30/13	HIM Project Team
404		Payment Systems	120 days	Wed 11/14/12	Tue 4/30/13	IT Project Team
405		**Go-Live Training**	**155 days**	**Thu 1/24/13**	**Wed 8/28/13**	**HIM Project Lead**

ID		Task Name	Duration	Start	Finish	Resource Names
406		**Schedule Training**	**10 days**	**Thu 1/24/13**	**Wed 2/6/13**	**HIM Project Lead**
407		Coding Staff	10 days	Thu 1/24/13	Wed 2/6/13	HIM Project Team
408		Clinical Staff	10 days	Thu 1/24/13	Wed 2/6/13	Core Project Team
409		Medical Staff	10 days	Thu 1/24/13	Wed 2/6/13	Core Project Team
410		Patient Access	10 days	Thu 1/24/13	Wed 2/6/13	Core Project Team
411		Billing Resources	10 days	Thu 1/24/13	Wed 2/6/13	Core Project Team
412		**Attend/Provide Training**	**145 days**	**Thu 2/7/13**	**Wed 8/28/13**	**HIM Project Lead**
413		Coding Staff	145 days	Thu 2/7/13	Wed 8/28/13	HIM Project Team
414		Clinical Staff	145 days	Thu 2/7/13	Wed 8/28/13	Clinical Project Resource
415		Medical Staff	145 days	Thu 2/7/13	Wed 8/28/13	Medical Staff
416		Patient Access	145 days	Thu 2/7/13	Wed 8/28/13	Pt. Access Project Resource
417		Billing Resources	145 days	Thu 2/7/13	Wed 8/28/13	Finance Project Resource
418		**Final Go-Live Preparation Activities**	**108 days**	**Wed 5/1/13**	**Fri 9/27/13**	
419		People	22 days	Thu 8/29/13	Fri 9/27/13	Core Project Team
420		Processes	22 days	Thu 8/29/13	Fri 9/27/13	Core Project Team
421		Technology	108 days	Wed 5/1/13	Fri 9/27/13	Core Project Team
422	🗓	**Implementation Go-Live**	**16 days**	**Tue 10/1/13**	**Tue 10/22/13**	**Steering Committee**
423		Code Charts Using ICD-10-CM and ICD-10-PCS Codes	1 day	Tue 10/1/13	Tue 10/1/13	HIM Project Resource
424	🗓	**Transmit ICD-10-CM and ICD-10-PCS Data**	**5 days**	**Wed 10/2/13**	**Tue 10/8/13**	**Project Manager**
425	🗓	Internal Systems	5 days	Wed 10/2/13	Tue 10/8/13	IT Project Lead
426	🗓	External Systems	5 days	Wed 10/2/13	Tue 10/8/13	IT Project Lead
427		**Verify Data Transmits Correctly**	**5 days**	**Wed 10/9/13**	**Tue 10/15/13**	**IT Project Lead**
428	🗓	Internal Systems	5 days	Wed 10/9/13	Tue 10/15/13	IT Project Lead
429	🗓	External Systems	5 days	Wed 10/9/13	Tue 10/15/13	IT Project Lead
430		**Verify Reports Generate Correctly**	**5 days**	**Wed 10/16/13**	**Tue 10/22/13**	
431		Internal Systems	5 days	Wed 10/16/13	Tue 10/22/13	HIM Project Lead,IT Project Lead
432		External Systems	5 days	Wed 10/16/13	Tue 10/22/13	HIM Project Lead,IT Project Lead
433		**Post Implementation Activities**	**115 days**	**Wed 10/16/13**	**Tue 3/25/14**	**Executive Sponsor**
434		Evaluate Project Results	15 days	Wed 10/16/13	Tue 11/5/13	Core Project Team
435		**Complete Project De-Brief**	**10 days**	**Wed 11/6/13**	**Tue 11/19/13**	**Project Manager**
436		Review Success Criterias	5 days	Wed 11/6/13	Tue 11/12/13	Core Project Team
437		Identify Lessons Learned	10 days	Wed 11/6/13	Tue 11/19/13	Core Project Team
438		**Identify Operational On-going Changes**	**90 days**	**Wed 11/20/13**	**Tue 3/25/14**	**Executive Sponsor**
439		Data Management	90 days	Wed 11/20/13	Tue 3/25/14	IT Project Lead,Core Project Team
440		Operational Management	90 days	Wed 11/20/13	Tue 3/25/14	HIM Project Team,Core Project Team
441		Celebrate Project Success	1 day	Wed 11/20/13	Wed 11/20/13	Core Project Team,Steering Committee, Sponsor

ICD-10 Preparation Checklist

by Sue Bowman, RHIA, CCS, and Ann Zeisset, RHIT, CCS, CCS-P

Although the implementation date for ICD-10-CM and ICD-10-PCS (jointly referred to as "ICD-10" throughout the rest of this document) may still be several years away, it is not too early to begin planning for the transition, and even putting some of those plans in motion. A well-planned, well-managed implementation process will increase the chances of a smooth, successful transition. Experience in other countries has shown that early preparation is key to success. The best way to manage the challenges inherent in making a transition of this magnitude is to tackle them in a phased approach.

Some of the preparation activities necessary for implementation provide benefits to the organization even before ICD-10 is implemented, such as medical record documentation improvement strategies and efforts to expand coding staff knowledge and skills. Also, an early start allows for resource allocation, such as costs for systems changes and education as well as staff time devoted to implementation processes, to be spread over several years. Thus, many of the costs can be absorbed by existing annual budgets rather than requiring a large budgetary investment at one time.

Editor's note

This article updates information contained in "ICD-10 Preparation Checklist, parts 1 and 2," originally published in the June and July-August 2004 issues of the *Journal of AHIMA*.

The following checklist and proposed phased approach to implementation were prepared to guide healthcare organizations in planning and managing the transition toward ICD-10.

Phase 1—Impact Assessment

The first stage of preparation involves assessing the impact of the change to new coding systems and identifying key tasks and objectives. Major tasks in this phase include creating an implementation planning team; identifying and budgeting for required information system (IS) changes; and assessing, budgeting, and implementing clinician and code set user education.

Target Audience

Health information management (HIM) leadership team
Coding professionals
Senior management
Medical staff
Financial management (including accounting and billing personnel)
IS personnel
Clinical department managers
Other data users (e.g., quality management, utilization management, case management, performance improvement, tumor registry, trauma registry, research)
Vendors (contract coding, software developers)
Business associates (including payers)

Goals

Organizationwide Implementation Strategy

1. Establish an interdisciplinary steering committee to oversee ICD-10 implementation.

- The committee should include representation from HIM, including both an HIM services manager and a representative from the staff responsible for code assignment; senior management; medical staff; financial management; and IS.
- The leader of this committee should serve as the project manager throughout the course of the implementation process; an HIM background would be advantageous for this role.
- This project manager should serve as a positive change agent for ICD-10 implementation.
- The steering committee would develop the organization's ICD-10 implementation strategy and identify the actions, persons responsible, and deadlines for the various tasks required to complete the transition. In addition, this plan should include estimated budget needs for each year leading up to implementation, as well as any post-implementation budgetary issues (such as additional training needs or the need for contractors to assist with coding backlogs or resolution of identified post-implementation problems), for early financial planning.
- Conduct regularly scheduled standing meetings on a consistent basis to ensure communication among key stakeholders.

2. Create ICD-10 code set impact awareness throughout the organization.
   - Educate senior management, IS personnel, clinical department managers, and medical staff on the coming transition to ICD-10 and the necessity for this transition (e.g., department managers' meetings, medical staff meetings, specialized meetings with senior management and IS).
   - Educate senior management on:
     —value of new code sets
     —adoption and implementation process (including timeline)

—preparation and transition effects on organizational operations (e.g., systems changes, processes, policies and procedures)

—impact on coding productivity and accuracy

—budgetary considerations

- Educate the organization's clinical department managers about the:

  —value of new code sets

  —expected timeline for approval and implementation

  —differences between ICD-10-CM and ICD-10-PCS and how each is used

  —differences between legacy and new coding systems

  —impact on each particular department and budgetary considerations

- Educate medical staff on:

  —value of new code sets

  —expected timeline for approval and implementation

  —differences between legacy and new coding systems

  —implementation plan and how it can be adapted for use in their own practices

  —impact on individual physicians and their budgetary considerations

  —impact on documentation practices and the importance of a strategy for documentation improvement

- Once the notice of proposed rule-making (NPRM) is published that establishes the timeline and expected implementation date, educate all of the above on key provisions of this rule.

3. Employ change management strategies to minimize "fear of change" factor.

4. Assess organizational readiness for data standard changes, considering the impact on:

- Affected staff
- Information systems (affected systems, applications, databases)

- Documentation process and work flow
- Data availability and use
- Organizational capacity (including budget)

5. HIM managers and coding professionals should:

- Educate themselves on the benefits and value of ICD-10—particularly within the context of national healthcare data quality measurement initiatives.

- Understand the regulatory process for adoption, anticipated implementation timeline and variables affecting the timeline, and the ICD-10 implementation process so they can facilitate discussions, answer questions and act as a resource for others.

- Learn how ICD-10 fits within the overall electronic health record (EHR), the nationwide health information network (NHIN), and data quality initiatives.

- Learn the structure, organization, and unique features of ICD-10-CM and ICD-10-PCS and gain a moderate level of familiarity with the coding systems. Methods include, but are not limited to:
  —Attending educational sessions
    - audio conferences
    - convention presentations
    - local conference presentations
    - online training
  —Reading *Journal of AHIMA* and other pertinent publications, including but not limited to:
    - Pertinent feature articles
    - "Word from Washington" columns
    - E-alerts
    - E-HIM® Fundamentals columns
    - AHIMA Practice Briefs
    - CodeWrite newsletter
    - ICD-10 educational materials, such as the AHIMA book *ICD-10-CM and ICD-10-PCS Preview*

—Reviewing ICD-10 materials on Centers for Medicare & Medicaid Services (CMS) and National Center for Health Statistics (NCHS) Web sites:
- ICD-10-CM coding guidelines
- ICD-10-PCS reference manual
- Documentation and User's Guide for the general equivalence map between ICD-10-PCS and ICD-9-CM

—Participating in the AHIMA ICD-10 Implementation Community of Practice (CoP) (limited to AHIMA members).

—Monitoring the ICD-10 page of the AHIMA Web site, the AHIMA HIPAA CoP, and the AHIMA Coding CoP for important news and other relevant information (limited to AHIMA members).

—Reading the 2003 report "ICD-10-Field Testing Project, Report on Findings: Perceptions, Ideas, and Recommendations from Coding Professionals Across the Nation" by the American Hospital Association (AHA) and AHIMA in the FORE Library: HIM Body of Knowledge (BoK).

—Staying abreast of news/announcements provided by AHIMA in order to keep up-to-date on status of adoption/implementation.

6. Develop a budget for ICD-10 implementation.
- Identify the specific departmental budget(s) that will be responsible for the cost of systems changes, hardware and software upgrades, and education.
- Determine whether there will be a need for increased staffing or consulting services to assist with IS changes, coding backlogs, monitoring of coding accuracy, or to support other aspects of implementation.
- Total implementation costs should be allocated over a several year time frame to allow for the absorption of the costs.

7. Conduct a detailed assessment of staff education needs (for all staff) and determine budgetary estimates.
    - Identify educational needs of staff and determine the following:
      —Who needs education?
      —What type and level of education do they need?
    - The multiple categories of users of coded data require varying levels of education on the new coding systems. These categories of users include:
      —Coding professionals
      —Other HIM staff responsible for health record services
      —Billing
      —Accounting
      —Corporate compliance office
      —Auditors and/or consultants performing documentation or coding review
      —Clinicians
      —Clinical department managers
      —Quality management
      —Utilization management
      —Patient access and registration (if they are involved in medical necessity determinations)
      —Ancillary departments
      —Data quality management staff
      —Data security personnel
      —Data analysts working both inside and outside the organization
      —Researchers
      —Other data users (e.g., performance improvement)
      —IS personnel
      —Prepaid contract managers and negotiators
    - Determine the best method, in terms of a balance between effectiveness and cost, of providing education. There are numerous methods of providing education today, such as:
      —traditional face-to-face classroom teaching
      —audio conferences

> —CD-ROM or downloadable materials (self-directed learning)
>
> —Various forms of Web-based instruction (self-directed or instructor-led)

- Determine whether education will be provided through internal or external mechanisms, or both.

8. Evaluate current data flow, work flows, and operational processes to identify processes and reports that will be affected and determine opportunities for improvement.

9. Assess extent of changes to systems, processes, policies/procedures, and education needs; determine associated budgetary assessments and compare to initial budget estimates and make note of variances for planning purposes.

10. Assess impact on organizational operations of change to new coding systems, such as implementation costs beyond the investment associated with education and systems changes; this would provide an assessment of the total cost of ownership for this change.

- Assess loss of code assignment and claims submission productivity during the learning curve period for users of code sets.

- Educate data users (e.g., case management, utilization management, quality management, data analysts) on data comparability issues and impact on longitudinal data analysis.

- Educate data users on differences in classification of diseases and procedures in the new coding systems, including definitions and code category composition, in order to assess impact on data trends.

11. Assess status of payers' and other business associates' progress toward ICD-10 preparedness by confirming when they expect to be ready.

12. Provide senior management with regular updates as to project status.

13. Keep affected staff informed through frequent updates regarding progress, next steps, and issue identification and resolution.

Information Systems

1. Orient IS personnel on the specifications of the code sets that they will need to know to implement systems changes, including the logic and hierarchical structure of ICD-10-CM and ICD-10-PCS. The following questions should be addressed:

   - What is the character-length specification for ICD-10-CM and ICD-10-PCS codes?
   - Is it alphabetic, numeric, or a combination of both?
   - Are the alphabetic characters case-sensitive?
   - Does the code format include a decimal?
   - Can codes, descriptions, and applicable support documentation and guidelines be obtained in a machine-readable form?
   - What coding systems will it replace and when will it replace them?
   - Are forward and backward maps available between the legacy and new coding systems? If so what is the defined use case for each?
   - How many data management systems will be affected and what types of systems changes will need to be made? (see list of specific examples under no. 2 below)

2. Perform a comprehensive systems audit for ICD-10 compatibility

   - Inventory all databases and systems applications that use ICD-9-CM codes, giving consideration to:
     - —Use of application service provider vs. internally developed system interface and other affected software programs
     - —How are ICD-9-CM codes used in each system? Will ICD-10-CM or ICD-10-PCS codes serve the same

purpose and will a change in code sets impact the results?

—Where do the codes come from (e.g., manually entered versus imported from another system)?

—How quality of data is checked

—Interfaces between systems

- Map electronic data flow to inventory all reports that contain ICD-9-CM codes.
- Perform a detailed analysis of systems changes that need to occur. Prioritize sequence of systems changes and estimate cost of changes. Refine previous budgetary estimates as necessary.

  —Determine required software changes:
  - Field size expansion
  - Change to alphanumeric composition
  - Use of decimals
  - Complete redefinition of code values and their interpretation
  - Longer code descriptions
  - Edit and logic changes
  - Modifications of table structures
  - Expansion of flat files containing diagnosis codes
  - Systems interfaces

  —Assess the changes to the various systems and applications that use coded data that will need to be made, including:
  - EHR systems
  - Decision support systems
  - Billing systems
  - Clinical systems
  - Encoding software
  - Computer-assisted coding applications
  - Medical record abstracting systems
  - Registration and scheduling systems
  - Aggregate data reporting
  - Utilization management

- Quality management systems
- Case mix systems
- Accounting systems
- Case management systems
- Disease management systems
- Provider profiling systems
- Clinical protocols
- Test ordering systems
- Clinical systems
- Clinical reminder systems
- Performance measurement systems
- Medical necessity software

■ Determine length of time both legacy and new coding systems will need to be supported and whether system storage capacity will need to be increased. Types of support to be considered include:

—Systems vendors—is support for both legacy and new coding systems addressed in the contract? How long is support for both coding systems anticipated? What kind of support is needed?

—Internal IS department—how long will the ICD-9 coding system continue to be accessible and to whom will it be accessible (e.g., data analysis personnel may require access for a longer period of time than the coding or billing staff)? Is system storage capacity adequate or will it need to be increased?

—Data users—how long will legacy data need to be available for data analysis, research, etc.?

—Billing—legacy system will still be needed for old claims and re-bills.

—Coding professionals—knowledge of both coding systems will continue to be needed.

■ Determine which reports will require modification of format or layout.

■ Determine which forms will require redesign.

■ Conduct a data mapping overview.

- Identify new or upgraded hardware/software requirements and determine budgetary implications (e.g., larger computer monitors, more powerful hard drive).
    —If the coding process is currently manual (use of hard-copy code books), consideration should be given to using electronic tools (such as an encoder) when ICD-10 is implemented, which will result in additional hardware and software requirements; although it would be technically possible for coding professionals to use a paper-based version of ICD-10, given the size and structure of these systems, they would be easiest to use in an electronic format.
    —Will hardware upgrades be needed to ensure optimal system performance?
3. Determine vendor readiness and timelines for upgrading software to new coding systems and determine if upgrades are covered by any existing contracts.
    - Communicate with vendors of software that incorporates ICD codes to determine when upgrades reflecting the new coding systems will be ready and whether any cost for the upgrades will be passed on to the organization, and if so, the projected cost and in what year it will be incurred.
    - If necessary, include costs of upgrade in ICD-10 budget.
    - Contract renewals
    - Determine the anticipated timeline for testing the performance of the new code sets in your systems environment.
    - Work with vendors to coordinate installation of new or upgraded software.
    - Actively participate in any vendor user group meetings regarding ICD-10 implementation.
4. Build flexibility into systems currently under development to ensure ICD-10 and, when possible, the next version of ICD compatibility.

Education of Coding Professionals

1. Assess adequacy of staff knowledge and skills for translation of clinical data into codes for secondary use.

   ■ Evaluate coding personnel's baseline knowledge in skills to identify knowledge gaps in the areas of medical terminology, anatomy and physiology, pathophysiology, and pharmacology. Measuring coding professionals' baseline knowledge will shorten the learning curve, improve coding accuracy and productivity, prepare for educational needs, and accelerate the realization of benefits of the new coding systems. AHIMA plans to provide self-assessment tools and other resources suitable for skill assessment.

   ■ Review ICD-10-CM coding guidelines, ICD-10-PCS reference manual, and other ICD-10 educational materials to identify areas where increased clinical knowledge will be needed.

   ■ Use information from coding professional knowledge gap assessment to develop individualized education plans for improving clinical knowledge to ensure it meets the requirements of ICD-10-CM and ICD-10-PCS.

   ■ If outsourced staff are used for coding, communicate with the companies that provide these services concerning their plans for ICD-10-related training.

   ■ Consider having the coding personnel practice coding a few records using ICD-10-CM and ICD-10-PCS to increase familiarity with the new coding systems.

     —Download ICD-10-CM information at www.cdc.gov/ nchs/about/otheract/icd9/icd10cm.htm

     —Download ICD-10-PCS information at http://www. cms.hhs.gov/ICD9ProviderDiagnosticCodes/08_ ICD10.asp

Documentation Improvement

1. Conduct medical record documentation assessments through an internal or external review process.

   ■ Evaluate random samples of various types of medical records to determine adequacy of documentation to support the required level of detail in new coding systems. (AHIMA will be developing a clinical documentation assessment tool to assist with this process).

   ■ Identify documentation deficiencies and develop a priority list of diagnoses and procedures requiring more granularity or other changes in data capture and recording.

   ■ Identify target segments of medical staff that would benefit from focused education to adapt their documentation practices to what is required for the new systems.

2. Implement a documentation improvement program to address deficiencies identified during the review process and a plan to prevent recurrence.

   ■ Designate a physician champion to assist in physician education.

   ■ Identify target segments of medical staff that would benefit from focused education about their documentation practices.

   ■ Educate medical staff about medical record documentation requirements required by the new coding systems through specific examples, emphasizing the value of more concise data capture for optimal results and better data quality.

   ■ Monitor documentation for evidence of improvement, identify areas still requiring assistance, and educate medical staff to eliminate remaining deficiencies.

3. Report summary of documentation assessment related to the use of ICD-10 and the achieved progress in improvements to senior management.

Phase 2—Overall Implementation

This stage involves three major tasks: implementation of required IS changes, follow-up assessment of documentation practices, and increasing education of the organization's coding professionals. Also include any items carried over from Phase 1.

Target Audience

> HIM managers
> IS personnel
> Medical staff
> Coding professionals
> Business associates
> Vendors
> Data users

Goals

Organizationwide Implementation Strategy

1. Follow-up with readiness status of payers and other business associates by contacting payers and other business associates for an updated status on their progress toward preparing for ICD-10 implementation.
2. Develop strategies to minimize problems during transition.
   - Assess impact of reduced code assignment productivity on the organization's accounts receivable status.
     —What is the anticipated impact on code assignment through-put? (Implementation variables that can affect productivity include the amount and level of preparation, extent of coding staff education and credentials, individual code assignment experience and knowledge of anatomy and disease processes, extent of training, quality of medical record documentation, and organizational size and complexity.)

—How long is coding professional productivity expected to be reduced?

—What steps could be taken to reduce the impact of decreased coding professional productivity?

- Eliminate coding backlogs prior to ICD-10 implementation.
- Use outsourced personnel for coding to assist with workload during the initial implementation period.
- Prioritize medical records to be coded.
- Offer additional training prior to implementation to improve confidence levels and minimize slow downs.
- Initiate additional efforts to improve the clarity of medical record documentation.
- Supply electronic tools to support the code assignment process.

■ Assess impact of decreased coding accuracy.

—What is the anticipated impact on coding accuracy with the new code sets?

—How long is it expected to take for the coding professionals to achieve the same level of proficiency as with ICD-9-CM?

—What steps could be taken to improve coding accuracy?

- Additional education
- Increased monitoring during the initial implementation period. (It is important to consider whether the increased monitoring duties should be assumed by staff, or if it will it be necessary to contract with a consultant and how use of existing personnel for more frequent and complex assessment of code assignment impacts the overall workflow.)

■ Miscellaneous issues—Identify other potential problems during the transition and implement strategies to reduce potential negative impact.

3. Continue to assess the impact of changing coding systems.
   - Educate data users (e.g., case management, utilization management, quality management, data analysts) on differences in classification of diseases and procedures in the new coding systems, including definitions and code category composition, in order to assess impact on data trends (If not completed in Phase 1).
4. Revise processes, policies, and procedures as appropriate.
5. Provide senior management with regular updates.
6. Keep affected staff informed through frequent updates regarding progress, next steps, and issue identification and resolution.
7. Develop a detailed schedule leading up to the point of Go-Live in order to clearly articulate all key stakeholders' roles and responsibilities.

Information Systems

1. Follow up with system developers or suppliers regarding their readiness for incorporation of the new code sets.
   - Projected availability of upgrade (still on target with date indicated in Phase 1?)
2. Determine impact of coding system change on longitudinal data analysis.
   - Where will data mapping occur to link data between the legacy and new coding systems, and will outside assistance be needed to create specific mapping applications beyond the maps or crosswalks supplied by the code set developers? Mapping will be needed to cross-reference between pre- and post-crossover periods in order to understand the correlation of ICD-9-CM and ICD-10 data.
3. Modify the report formats and redesign the forms identified in Phase 1.

4. Implement and test systems changes, including both in-house and proprietary systems changes.
   - Implement identified in-house systems changes.
   - Begin testing both in-house and proprietary systems changes in a coordinated manner.
   - Test completed in-house changes.
   - Test information systems changes once the system developers have completed the changes.

Education of Coding Professionals

1. HIM coding staff should increase familiarity with the new coding systems and the associated coding guidelines.
   - Increase intensity of coder training on the new coding systems and coding guidelines.

Documentation Improvement

1. Continue to assess and improve medical record documentation practices.
   - Monitor medical record documentation practices.
   - Continue to work with clinicians to improve documentation in areas where deficiencies affect data integrity.

Phase 3—Go-Live Preparation

This stage involves several major tasks: finalization of systems changes, testing of claims transactions with payers, intensive education of the organization's coding professionals, monitoring coding accuracy and reimbursement with prospective payment systems results, including the Diagnosis Related Group (DRG) assignment. Also include any items carried over from Phase 2.

Target Audience

HIM managers
Information systems personnel

Payers

Coding professionals

Vendors

Financial management (including accounting and billing
personnel)

Goals

Organizationwide Implementation Strategy

1. Conduct testing of claims transactions with payers.
   - Six months prior to implementation, test ICD-10 components of claims transactions with payers.
2. Assess potential reimbursement impact of new coding systems.
   - Evaluate potential DRG shifts.
   - Evaluate changes in case mix index.
   - Communicate with payers on anticipated changes in reimbursement schedules or payment policies.
3. Provide senior management with regular updates as to project status.
4. Keep key staff informed through frequent updates regarding progress, next steps, and issue identification and resolution. This could be initially conducted through weekly meetings, e-mail communications, with more frequent communication (perhaps daily) as the Go-Live date gets closer.
5. Review and modify the detailed schedule leading up to the point of Go-Live in order to clearly articulate all key stakeholders' roles and responsibilities during the last couple of weeks.

Information Systems

1. Finalize systems changes and complete testing of these changes.
   - Complete all necessary in-house systems changes.

■ Confirm with vendor(s) that changes/upgrades in vendor systems have been completed.

■ Finish testing the changes.

■ Make modifications in response to the results of the testing and conduct regression testing.

Education of Coding Professionals

1. Complete intensive coding professional education and education of other users previously identified as requiring education.

   ■ Three to six months prior to implementation, all coding staff should complete intensive education on applying the new coding systems (the estimated amount of training is 24-40 hours, depending on whether coding professionals require both ICD-10-CM and ICD-10-PCS education).

   ■ Document completion of this training in personnel files.

   ■ To ensure the quality and consistency of ICD-10 education, it is recommended that training be conducted by an AHIMA-certified trainer.

   ■ Sources of training include:
     —Distance education courses
     —Audio seminars or Web-based in-services
     —Self-directed learning using printed materials or electronic tools
     —Traditional classroom training by a certified trainer

   ■ Communicate with companies supplying contracted coding staff to ensure they have received the necessary education and ask for documentation to confirm that training has occurred and has been provided by a qualified source (e.g., AHIMA-certified trainer).

   ■ Implement the identified education plan for users of coded data and document completion of the training in their personnel files.

GO LIVE!

Phase 4—Post-implementation

This phase consists of monitoring coding accuracy for reimbursement, and other data management impact, coding productivity and continuing with appropriate coding professional training.

Target Audience

HIM managers

Information systems personnel

Payers

Coding professionals

Medical staff

Senior management

Others, depending on identified problems to be resolved

Financial management (including accounting and billing personnel)

Goals

Organizationwide Implementation Strategy

1. The ICD-10 steering committee should continue to meet regularly to share information regarding implementation progress, including monitoring of the status of issue resolution, discussing lessons learned, and identifying best practices. These meetings should continue until the committee feels they are no longer necessary.

2. Keep key staff informed regarding issue identification and resolution through weekly updates or institution of a Web-based issue tracking system that would allow staff to check the status of an issue at any time.

3. Train or re-train staff; continue budgetary planning for training of staff.
   - Train new staff.
   - Train staff unavailable during previous training.
   - Provide re-training or additional training as needed.
4. Assess the reimbursement impact of the new system, provide education to staff on reimbursement issues, and monitor case mix and reimbursement group (e.g., DRGs) assignment.
   - Work closely with payers to resolve payment issues, such as claims denials or rejections.
   - Communicate with payers on anticipated changes in reimbursement schedules or payment policies.
   - Analyze changes in case mix index.
   - Concurrently review case mix or reimbursement groups (e.g., DRGs, HHRGs) and diagnosis and procedure code assignments.
   - Analyze shifts in reimbursement groups.
   - Provide education and feedback regarding reimbursement issues to staff.
5. Resolve post-implementation problems as expeditiously as possible.
   - The interdisciplinary steering committee should follow up on post-implementation problems, such as claims denials or rejections or coding backlogs.
   - Work with internal staff or external entities as appropriate to resolve problems as expeditiously as possible.
6. Monitor coding professional productivity.
   - Develop plans to address coding professional backlogs such as contracting to outsource coding professionals.
7. Maintain communication with payers and resolve any problems.
8. Keep senior management informed of identified issues and progress in resolving them through pre-scheduled standing meetings or weekly updates.

Information Systems

1. Monitor and respond to any information systems problems or issues.

Education of Coding Professionals

1. Post-implementation, monitor coding accuracy closely and initiate corrective action as necessary, such as providing additional education.

Documentation Improvement

1. Continue to monitor medical record documentation and work with medical staff on documentation improvement strategies if needed.

Acknowledgements

June Bronnert, RHIA, CCS, CCS-P
Donald T. Mon, PhD
Rita Scichilone, MHSA, RHIA, CCS, CCS-P
Allison Viola, MBA, RHIA

Reference

AHIMA's Coding Products and Services Team. "Destination 10: Healthcare Organization Preparation for ICD-10-CM and ICD-10-PCS." (AHIMA Practice Brief). *Journal of AHIMA* 75, no.3 (March 2004): 56A-D.

Source

Bowman, Sue, and Ann Zeisset. "ICD-10 Preparation Checklist" (Updated June 2007)

Go-Live Plan

Project Information

Project Manager
Budget Manager
Project Sponsor
Project Start Date mm/dd/yyyy
Last Modified Date mm/dd/yyyy

Introduction

The following Go-Live plan details all activities that will be performed for the Implementation and Go-Live activities to implement ICD-10-CM and ICD-10-PCS code sets. The Go-Live activities will take place at the following facility:

Facility Name
Facility Address
City, State Zip Code

At the following locations:

- *HIM Department*
- *IS Department*
- *Cardiology Department*
- *Technology Lab, 3rd Floor, Room B*

193

Go-Live Activity Participant List

Name	Contact Phone	E-Mail Address	Project Role	Organization (Facility/Vendor/ Contractor)

Go-Live Roles and Responsibilities

Owner	Role	Responsibility
First Name Last Name	Executive Sponsor	Ensure all resources are available and on target for Go-Live activities
First Name Last Name	Project Manager— Facility	• Develop, manage, and distribute project plan documents and schedules, including budget, throughout project • Develop and distribute communication plan and activities—e-mails, marketing materials (such as posters, meetings, handouts, pocket documentation) • Oversee all Go-Live activities to be completed on time and on budget • Develop support groups made up of team members, end-users, and customers
First Name Last Name	Project Lead—HIM	• Complete project tasks on time and on budget • Provide ICD-10-CM and ICD-10-PCS training as required • Provide End-User support regarding HIM and Coding-related activities throughout project • Communicate issues and concerns with the Facility Project Manager
First Name Last Name	Project Lead—IS	• Complete project tasks on time and on budget • Provide technology education and training as required • Provide End-User support regarding software systems and associated applications throughout project • Communicate issues and concerns with the Facility Project Manager

Go-Live Roles and Responsibilities *(continued)*

Owner	Role	Responsibility
First Name Last Name	Project Manager— Vendor A	• Provide project resources to complete project activities for X applications and systems • Ensure deliverables are provided on time, within budget, and as outlined in the Business Requirements and Contract terms • Communicate issues and concerns with the Facility Project Manager
First Name Last Name	Project Manager— Vendor B	• Provide project resources to complete project activities for X applications and systems • Ensure deliverables are provided on time, within budget, and as outlined in the Business Requirements and Contract terms • Communicate issues and concerns with the Facility Project Manager
First Name Last Name	Project Manager— Vendor C	• Provide project resources to complete project activities for X applications and systems • Ensure deliverables are provided on time, within budget, and as outlined in the Business Requirements and Contract terms • Communicate issues and concerns with the Facility Project Manager
First Name Last Name	Facility Interface and Software Support	• Complete project activities related to Interface development, testing, monitoring, and deployment. • Provide application support to testing team and end-users • Communicate issues and concerns with the Facility Project Manager
First Name Last Name	Facility Network and Hardware Support	• Provide deployment support for hardware, software, workstations, and network configurations • Communicate issues and concerns with the Facility Project Manager

Go-Live Roles and Responsibilities *(continued)*

Owner	Role	Responsibility
First Name Last Name	Vendor A— Application and Process Support	• Complete project tasks on time and on budget • Provide training as required on the applications • Provide End-User application support throughout project • Communicate issues and concerns with the Facility Project Manager
First Name Last Name	Vendor B— Application and Process Support	• Complete project tasks on time and on budget • Provide training as required on the applications • Provide End-User application support throughout project • Communicate issues and concerns with the Facility Project Manager
First Name Last Name	Vendor C— Application and Process Support	• Complete project tasks on time and on budget • Provide training as required on the applications • Provide End-User application support throughout project • Communicate issues and concerns with the Facility Project Manager
First Name Last Name	ICD-10-CM, ICD-10-PCS Training	• Provide training to internal resources as required • End-User Support throughout project and Go-Live activities • Communicate issues and concerns with the Facility Project Manager
First Name Last Name	Additional Role	Additional Responsibilities

Tools and Resources Needed Per Project Phase

Phase I: Version 5010 (some healthcare transactions) and Version D.0 (pharmacy transactions) compliance—January 1, 2012

- Test system configured with v5010 and vD.0 compliance
- End-users able to begin testing v5010 and vD.0 transmissions
- Application support resources able to resolve issues with v5010 and/or vD.0 transmissions
- Workstations linked to test systems
- IS resources for Network Support
- HIM resources for HIM/Coding questions
- Billing/Finance Resources for results verification
- Additional Resources

Phase II: Version 3.0 (Medicaid pharmacy subrogation transaction) compliance—January 1, 2012

- Test System Configured with v3.0 compliance
- End-users able to begin testing v3.0 transmissions
- Application support resources able to resolve issues with v3.0 transmissions
- Workstations linked to test systems
- IS Resources for network support
- HIM Resources for HIM/Coding questions
- Billing/Finance resources for results verification
- Additional resources

Phase III: ICD-10-CM and ICD-10-PCS compliance— October 1, 2013

- Test system configured for ICD-10-CM and ICD-10-PCS compliance
- End-users able to begin testing ICD-10-CM and ICD-10-PCS transmissions
- Application support resources able to resolve issues with ICD-10-CM, ICD-10-PCS, and ICD-9-CM transmissions
- Workstations linked to test systems
- IS resources for network support
- HIM resources for HIM/Coding questions
- Billing/Finance resources for results verification
- Additional resources

Go-Live Key Milestones

✓	Project Milestones	Responsible Party	Due Date
	Develop Project Strategy and Plans	Name	mm/dd/yyyy
	Assign Project Resources	Name	mm/dd/yyyy
	Approve Preliminary Project Schedule and Budget	Name	mm/dd/yyyy
	Complete Assessment Activities (Gap Analysis)	Name	mm/dd/yyyy
	Review Assessment Findings	Name	mm/dd/yyyy
	Complete Vendor Contract Modifications and Additions	Name	mm/dd/yyyy
	Approve Updated Project Schedule and Budget	Name	mm/dd/yyyy
	Begin System Modifications Phase I: v5010, vD.0	Name	mm/dd/yyyy
	Begin System Modifications Phase II: v3.0	Name	mm/dd/yyyy
	Complete System Modifications Phase I: v5010, vD.0	Name	mm/dd/yyyy
	Complete System Modifications Phase II: v3.0	Name	mm/dd/yyyy
	Begin Internal Testing and Modification Activities Phase I: v5010, vD.0	Name	mm/dd/yyyy
	Begin Internal Testing and Modification Activities Phase II: v3.0	Name	mm/dd/yyyy
	Complete Internal Testing and Modification Activities Phase I: v5010, vD.0	Name	mm/dd/yyyy
	Complete Internal Testing and Modification Activities Phase II: v3.0	Name	mm/dd/yyyy
	Begin External Testing Activities Phase I: v5010, vD.0	Name	mm/dd/yyyy
	Begin External Testing Activities Phase II: v3.0	Name	mm/dd/yyyy
	Begin Internal Orientation for Phase III: ICD-10-CM and ICD-10-PCS	Name	mm/dd/yyyy
	Begin System Modifications Phase III: ICD-10-CM and ICD-10-PCS	Name	mm/dd/yyyy

Go–Live Key Milestones *(continued)*

✓	Project Milestones	Responsible Party	Due Date
	Begin External Testing and Modification Activities Phase I: v5010, vD.0	Name	mm/dd/yyyy
	Begin External Testing and Modification Activities Phase II: v3.0	Name	mm/dd/yyyy
	Complete External Testing and Modification Activities Phase I: v5010, vD.0	Name	mm/dd/yyyy
	Complete External Testing and Modification Activities Phase II: v3.0	Name	mm/dd/yyyy
	Complete System Modifications Phase III: ICD-10-CM and ICD-10-PCS	Name	mm/dd/yyyy
	Begin Internal Testing and Modification Activities Phase III: ICD-10-CM and ICD-10-PCS	Name	mm/dd/yyyy
	Prepare for Go–Live Activities Phase I: v5010, vD.0	Name	mm/dd/yyyy
	Prepare for Go–Live Activities Phase II: v3.0	Name	mm/dd/yyyy
	Complete Go–Live Activities Phase I: v5010, vD.0	Name	mm/dd/yyyy
	Complete Go–Live Activities Phase II: v3.0	Name	mm/dd/yyyy
	Report on Post Go–Live Activities Phase I: v5010, vD.0	Name	mm/dd/yyyy
	Report on Post Go–Live Activities Phase II: v3.0	Name	mm/dd/yyyy
	Complete Internal Testing and Modification Activities Phase III: ICD-10-CM and ICD-10-PCS	Name	mm/dd/yyyy
	Prepare for Go–Live Activities Phase III: ICD-10-CM and ICD-10-PCS	Name	mm/dd/yyyy
	Complete Go–Live Activities Phase III: ICD-10-CM and ICD-10-PCS	Name	mm/dd/yyyy
	Report on Post Go–Live Activities Phase III: ICD-10-CM and ICD-10-PCS	Name	mm/dd/yyyy

Go-Live Activity Timeline

Detail every task to be completed each day for the duration of the Go-Live activities within the project phase.

Phase I

	Time	Task	Responsible Party
Date			
	XX:XX AM/PM		Name
	XX:XX AM/PM		Name
	XX:XX AM/PM		Name
Date			
	XX:XX AM/PM		Name
	XX:XX AM/PM		Name
	XX:XX AM/PM		Name
Date			
	XX:XX AM/PM		Name
	XX:XX AM/PM		Name
	XX:XX AM/PM		Name
Date			
	XX:XX AM/PM		Name
	XX:XX AM/PM		Name
	XX:XX AM/PM		Name

Phase II

	Time	Task	Responsible Party
Date			
	XX:XX AM/PM		Name
	XX:XX AM/PM		Name
	XX:XX AM/PM		Name
Date			
	XX:XX AM/PM		Name
	XX:XX AM/PM		Name
	XX:XX AM/PM		Name
Date			
	XX:XX AM/PM		Name
	XX:XX AM/PM		Name
	XX:XX AM/PM		Name
Date			
	XX:XX AM/PM		Name
	XX:XX AM/PM		Name
	XX:XX AM/PM		Name

Phase III

	Time	Task	Responsible Party
Date			
	XX:XX AM/PM		Name
	XX:XX AM/PM		Name
	XX:XX AM/PM		Name
Date			
	XX:XX AM/PM		Name
	XX:XX AM/PM		Name
	XX:XX AM/PM		Name
Date			
	XX:XX AM/PM		Name
	XX:XX AM/PM		Name
	XX:XX AM/PM		Name
Date			
	XX:XX AM/PM		Name
	XX:XX AM/PM		Name
	XX:XX AM/PM		Name

Communication Plan

The project team participating in the Go-Live activities can be reached by the numbers provided in the participant's section. The following phone trees listed below outline the procedure of updates and communications regarding daily activities and issues as well as the successful completion of the Go-Live activities.

Phase I: v5010, vD.0
Implementation Update Phone Tree for Go-Live Activities

At *XX:XX* AM/PM daily/weekly *Name (Resource A)* will contact:
Name (Resource B/Facility Project Manager)   *Project Role*

Name (Resource B) will then contact:
Name (Resource C)   *Project Role*

Name (Resource B) will then e-mail:
Core Project Team   Via e-mail
Vendor A Project Team   Via e-mail
Vendor B Project Team   Via e-mail
Vendor C Project Team   Via e-mail

Issue or Problem Phone Tree:
If any issues or problems arise *Name (Resource B/Facility Project Manager)* will contact:

Name (Resource A)   *Project Role*
Core Project Team   Via e-mail
Vendor A Project Team   Via e-mail
Vendor B Project Team   Via e-mail
Vendor C Project Team   Via e-mail

Name (Resource A) will then contact:
Name (Resource C)   *Project Role*

Successful Completion Phone Tree:
Once all Go-Live activities have been completed successfully for Phase I, *Name (Resource B/Facility Project Manager)* will contact:

Name (Resource C)   *Project Role*
Core Project Team   Via e-mail
Vendor A Project Team   Via e-mail
Vendor B Project Team   Via e-mail
Vendor C Project Team   Via e-mail
All Steering Committee Resources   Via e-mail

Phase II: v3.0
Implementation Update Phone Tree for Go-Live Activities

At *XX:XX* AM/PM daily/weekly *Name (Resource A)* will contact:
Name (Resource B/Facility Project Manager)   *Project Role*

Name (Resource B) will then contact:
Name (Resource C)   *Project Role*

Name (Resource B) will then e-mail:
Core Project Team   Via e-mail
Vendor A Project Team   Via e-mail
Vendor B Project Team   Via e-mail
Vendor C Project Team   Via e-mail

Issue or Problem Phone Tree:
If any issues or problems arise *Name (Resource B/Facility Project Manager)* will
contact:

Name (Resource A)   *Project Role*
Core Project Team   Via e-mail
Vendor A Project Team   Via e-mail
Vendor B Project Team   Via e-mail
Vendor C Project Team   Via e-mail

Name (Resource A) will then contact:
Name (Resource C)   *Project Role*

Successful Completion Phone Tree:
Once all Go-Live activities have been completed successfully for Phase I,
Name (Resource B/Facility Project Manager) will contact:

Name (Resource C)   *Project Role*
Core Project Team   Via e-mail
Vendor A Project Team   Via e-mail
Vendor B Project Team   Via e-mail
Vendor C Project Team   Via e-mail
All Steering Committee Resources   Via e-mail

Phase III: ICD-10-CM and ICD-10-PCS
Implementation Update Phone Tree for Go-Live Activities

At *XX:XX* AM/PM daily/weekly *Name (Resource A)* will contact:
Name (Resource B/Facility Project Manager)   *Project Role*

Name (Resource B) will then contact:
Name (Resource C)   *Project Role*

Name (Resource B) will then e-mail:
Core Project Team   Via e-mail
Vendor A Project Team   Via e-mail
Vendor B Project Team   Via e-mail
Vendor C Project Team   Via e-mail

Issue or Problem Phone Tree:
If any issues or problems arise *Name (Resource B/Facility Project Manager)* will
contact:

Name (Resource A)   *Project Role*
Core Project Team   Via e-mail
Vendor A Project Team   Via e-mail
Vendor B Project Team   Via e-mail
Vendor C Project Team   Via e-mail

Name (Resource A) will then contact:
Name (Resource C)   *Project Role*

Successful Completion Phone Tree:
Once all Go-Live activities have been completed successfully for Phase I,
Name (Resource B/Facility Project Manager) will contact:

Name (Resource C)   *Project Role*
Core Project Team   Via e-mail
Vendor A Project Team   Via e-mail
Vendor B Project Team   Via e-mail
Vendor C Project Team   Via e-mail
All Steering Committee Resources   Via e-mail

Go-Live Activities Back-out Plan

A decision should be made to back out of the Go-Live activities for each Phase by the following dates:

Phase I: XX:XX AM/PM on Date.
Phase II: XX:XX AM/PM on Date.
Phase III: XX:XX AM/PM on Date.

A decision to back out of planned activities will be made by the Core Team members, at which time it will take approximately two hours to identify and determine what the issue is and make the final decision on whether or not to back out of continued Go-Live activities. In the case of a back out, the users will complete the following activities:

• Activity X
• Activity Y
• Activity Z

Once the Core Project team has identified a resolution to the issue, a communication will be sent to all team members stating the next steps or alternate Go-Live activity plan, including date and time for the continued activities.

Go-Live Activity Support

Go-Live activities will be supported by the following resources based on the schedule as follows:

Phase I

Time	Name	Project Role	Contact Number
8:30 am–5:00 pm	*Name*	*Project Role*	xxx-xxx-xxxx
8:30 am–5:00 pm	*Name*	*Project Role*	xxx-xxx-xxxx
8:30 am–5:00 pm	*Name*	*Project Role*	xxx-xxx-xxxx
8:30 am–5:00 pm	*Name*	*Project Role*	xxx-xxx-xxxx
8:30 am–5:00 pm	*Name*	*Project Role*	xxx-xxx-xxxx
8:30 am–5:00 pm	*Name*	*Project Role*	xxx-xxx-xxxx
8:30 am–5:00 pm	*Name*	*Project Role*	xxx-xxx-xxxx

Phase II

Time	Name	Project Role	Contact Number
8:30 am–5:00 pm	*Name*	*Project Role*	xxx-xxx-xxxx
8:30 am–5:00 pm	*Name*	*Project Role*	xxx-xxx-xxxx
8:30 am–5:00 pm	*Name*	*Project Role*	xxx-xxx-xxxx
8:30 am–5:00 pm	*Name*	*Project Role*	xxx-xxx-xxxx
8:30 am–5:00 pm	*Name*	*Project Role*	xxx-xxx-xxxx
8:30 am–5:00 pm	*Name*	*Project Role*	xxx-xxx-xxxx
8:30 am–5:00 pm	*Name*	*Project Role*	xxx-xxx-xxxx

Phase III

Time	Name	Project Role	Contact Number
8:30 am–5:00 pm	*Name*	*Project Role*	xxx-xxx-xxxx
8:30 am–5:00 pm	*Name*	*Project Role*	xxx-xxx-xxxx
8:30 am–5:00 pm	*Name*	*Project Role*	xxx-xxx-xxxx
8:30 am–5:00 pm	*Name*	*Project Role*	xxx-xxx-xxxx
8:30 am–5:00 pm	*Name*	*Project Role*	xxx-xxx-xxxx
8:30 am–5:00 pm	*Name*	*Project Role*	xxx-xxx-xxxx
8:30 am–5:00 pm	*Name*	*Project Role*	xxx-xxx-xxxx

Problem Reporting Guide

Issues identified during the Go-Live activities should be reported immediately to the following resources:

Project Phase	Software System/ Application	Resource Name	Project Role	Communication Method
Phase I	*Name*	*Name*	*Project Role*	e-mail, Web site, etc.
	Name	*Name*	*Project Role*	e-mail, Web site, etc.
	Name	*Name*	*Project Role*	e-mail, Web site, etc.
Phase II	*Name*	*Name*	*Project Role*	e-mail, Web site, etc.
	Name	*Name*	*Project Role*	e-mail, Web site, etc.
	Name	*Name*	*Project Role*	e-mail, Web site, etc.
Phase III	*Name*	*Name*	*Project Role*	e-mail, Web site, etc.
	Name	*Name*	*Project Role*	e-mail, Web site, etc.
	Name	*Name*	*Project Role*	e-mail, Web site, etc.

All issues identified during the Go-Live activities to be reported should include the following information:

- User experiencing the issue
- Application experiencing the issue
- Date issue was experienced
- Location of testing/issue identification
- Error code/message, identification information
- Unexpected results
- Expected results
- Steps taken when error/unexpected results was received
- Additional comments
- Attach a screen print if possible

Notes

Notes

Resources

ICD-10-CM/PCS and 5010 Official Web sites

Centers for Disease Control

National Center for Health Statistics Official Guidelines for ICD-10-CM.
http://www.cdc.gov/nchs/about/otheract/icd9/icd10cm.htm

ICD-10-CM International Classification of Diseases

This is the link for the 2009 ICD-10-CM code set.
http://www.cdc.gov/nchs/about/otheract/icd9/icd10cm.htm

ICD-10-PCS information

This is the link for the 2009 ICD-10-PCS code set.
http://www.cms.hhs.gov/ICD10/01m_2009_ICD10PCS.asp#TopOfPage

X12 version 5010

This is the link for the official site of the Accredited Standards Committee
    (ASC), which includes 5010/D.0 implementation guides, educational
    products and services.
http://www.x12.org/x12org/index.cfm

Regulations

Final Rules

ICD-10-CM/PCS adoption and modifications to electronic transaction
    standards
http://www.cms.hhs.gov/TransactionCodeSetsStands/
02_TransactionsandCodeSetsRegulations.asp

US federal government search engine

Type in "ICD-10" for ICD-10 contents and "(HIPAA) Electronic Transaction Standards" for X12 5010 contents.

www.regulations.gov

Resources

AHA

ICD-10 Resource Center

ICD-10 news updates and presentations from CMS, ICD-9-CM Coordination and Maintenance Committee, AHA, NUBC, and WHO.

http://www.ahacentraloffice.com/ahacentraloffice_app/ICD-10/resources.jsp

AHIMA

How to prepare for ICD-10 and frequently asked questions.

http://www.ahima.org/icd10/

CMS

5010 resource center

Electronic billing and electronic data interchange transactions.

http://www.cms.hhs.gov/ElectronicBillingEDITrans/18_5010D0.
asp#TopOfPagePreparation

Announcements

http://www.cms.hhs.gov/ICD10/06_Announcements_and_Communications.
asp#TopOfPage

ICD-9-CM Coordination and Maintenance Committee

http://www.cms.hhs.gov/ICD10/08_ICD9CM_Coordination_and_
Maintenance_Committee_Meetings.asp#TopOfPage

Educational Resources

Free educational tools, such as brochures, DVDs, fact sheets, and other downloads, via the Medicare Learning Network.

http://www.cms.hhs.gov/ICD10/05_Educational_Resources.asp#TopOfPage

Ingenix

Informational and educational resources.
www.icd10prepared.com

Washington Publishing Company (WPC)

Information regarding electronic data exchange standards.
http://www.wpc-edi.com/content/view/579/387/

3M

ICD-10: Prepare now for 2013

http://solutions.3m.com/wps/portal/3M/en_US/3M_Health_Information_
   Systems/HIS/Resources/ICD-10/

I
N
D
E
X